INTRODUCTION TO CELL AND MOLECULAR BIOLOGY

by
K. SATHASIVAN

Contents

1. INTRODUCTION TO BIOLOGY

Concepts
1. Biological systems are structured at many levels that interrelate and interact.
2. Cells and organisms are made of organic molecules with specific properties and water.
3. Scientific methods validate predictions through experimentation by testing a hypothesis and finding substantial evidence.

Outline
I. Why study biology
II. What is life
III. How to study life
IV. Classification system in biology

I.   WHY STUDY BIOLOGY

Understanding life processes: The study of biology helps us understand the nature of life and the mechanisms underlying life processes.
Application of the knowledge: We can use the knowledge for survival, improvement of life, such as finding new cures for diseases and developing better plants for agriculture, or improving the environment.

Why biology is increasingly important today
The last few centuries were dominated by major discoveries in chemistry and physics. The 21st century will see a major impact by the explosion of information from researches in various disciplines of biological sciences merging with knowledge from other fields.
More than half a million papers are being published per year in biology alone. DNA, the secret code of life, was discovered only six decades ago, but we have sequenced the entire human genome and we are able to genetically modify many organisms. Applications are rapidly increasing in various fields including medical, agricultural and veterinary sciences.

Why study cellular and molecular biology
The connecting basis of all life is at the cell and molecular level. DNA to RNA to protein and the cellular mechanisms form the fundamental basis of life. Many biological phenomena are better understood at the biochemical and molecular level. It provides an opportunity to genetically alter DNA, develop cures and diagnostics to improve life in a very fundamental and precise way. To study biology, we should start with the properties of living organisms, selected model systems and some broad approaches to study life.

II.   WHAT IS LIFE

Life as we know is carbon based, organic in nature and contains water. The basic unit of life is the cell. The emergent properties of living organisms are as follows.

1. Reproduction: Life comes only from another life. The genetic material in all living cells is made of DNA.
2. Growth and development: All living organisms go through growth and developmental stages.
3. Order and Structure: Living cells and organisms are highly ordered and structured. The structure correlates with function.
4. Metabolism: Energy consumption and release happen constantly in a living organism. They consume organic foods, minerals and other nutrients. They can make and breakdown large molecules through various metabolic processes.
5. Respiration: It is an essential process in this energy consumption and release. Living organisms breathe in oxygen and release carbon dioxide to generate energy.
6. Response to environmental stimuli: The living organisms can sense (the surroundings) environmental cues and respond in an appropriate way. They can maintain internal conditions (homeostasis) in spite of changing surroundings.
7. Adaptation and evolution: Living organisms adapt to their environment over short periods of their generation or over many generations. Over billions of years, life has adapted, changed and evolved

1

to make new life forms.

8. Autonomous movement: Living organisms such as bacteria, protists and animals can move autonomously. Fungi and plants normally grow towards sources of nutrition and/or light.

III.   HOW TO STUDY LIFE

Model systems: Since there are millions of living organisms, we cannot study every one of them in a detailed manner. Hence, we use selected organisms known as model systems to study the mechanism of life. A model system is a representative organism or a cell type used for conducting simple to complex biological experiments. Model systems are normally easy to grow, manipulate and study. A vast amount of genetic information is already available from published studies about them.

Examples of model systems

Prokaryotes:	(unicellular and cells with no nucleus) E. coli (*Escherichia coli*) Salmonella (*Salmonella typhimurium*)
Eukaryotes:	(unicellular & multicellular organisms with a membrane bound nucleus in their cells)
Plants:	Arabidopsis (*Arabidopsis thaliana*) Corn (*Zea mays*) *and* Rice (*Oryza sativa*)
Fungi:	Yeast (*Saccharomyces cerevisiae*)
Animals:	Fruit fly (*Drosophila melanogaster*) Nematode (*Caenorhabditis elegans*) Mouse (*Mus musculus*) *and* Zebra fish (*Danio rerio*) Human cell lines. (He la cells)

Broad Approaches to Study Life

Based on whether an entire organism or a part of an organism is used in an experiment, we can call the studies as either holistic or reductionist. *[handwritten: whole]*

Holism: An approach to study whole organisms for behavioral, physiological and nutritional studies. For example, rats are used as a model system to study the effect of various drugs on aging.

Reductionism: An approach to study multicellular organisms at cellular or tissue levels or even at the molecular level. Whole organisms are not used. Cells or tissues derived from the organisms are used to conduct experiments. For example, various cell lines of humans and cell suspensions of higher plants are used for cellular, biochemical and molecular studies.

Another way to describe a study is based on whether the experiment is done under living or non-living conditions. The following terms describe the broad experimental methods.

In vivo studies are used to study physiology, ecology of organisms under living conditions. Examples: rats, rabbits, plant tissue culture etc. These studies can be holistic or reductionist using cells or tissues. *[handwritten: living]*

In vitro studies include experiments performed under non-living (abiotic) conditions, i.e. in a test tube with known quantities of chemicals and enzymes added and incubated at a particular temperature, pH etc. Such systems are used to study biochemistry, cell biology and molecular biology. These studies are strictly reductionistic in approach. *[handwritten: abiotic]*

In situ studies refer to experiments conducted to determine the presence of certain molecules such as DNA, RNA or protein in a particular site (say within a cell or tissue). For example, Fluorescent in situ hybridization (FISH) is used to determine which chromosome contains a particular gene. These are normally in vitro studies based on reductionism.

In silico studies: These are based on computer analysis of data to draw conclusions or identify patterns in genome or gene expression studies. These are becoming common with vast amount of genome and proteome data accumulated by sequencing DNA and proteins from many organisms. These come under the field of bioinformatics or computational biology.

Scientific Reasoning

A scientific process usually starts with a hypothesis (a prediction that can be properly tested) followed by experimentation with proper controls allowing conclusions to be drawn. The conclusions can be made using an inductive or deductive approach.

Inductive approach:
Specific conclusions and observations are used to make generalization. For example, based on observing various species, Darwin was able to formulate a general concept of evolution.

Deductive approach: General concepts are used to deduce specific conclusions. For example, based on the fact that all birds have feathers, you can say that if "peacock" is a bird, it should have feathers. Hypotheses are formed based on observations and they must be testable. Experiments must be conducted in a controlled way with proper treatments and controls. The treatments may include positive (has been tested and shown to work) and negative (should not work) controls. For example, if you are conducting experiments on new antibiotics to kill *E. coli* then you will plate the bacteria in proper medium, each of them mixed with the different kinds of new antibiotics in separate plates. The positive control will have a known antibiotic and a negative control will be without any antibiotic.
Once the results of an experiment are repeated by several scientists under various conditions, then they may be used to form a theory, if it is a unifying concept. If it is confirmed that they are proven true at all times, it may lead to a law.

IV.   CLSSIFICATION SYSTEM

Taxonomic Classification:
A standard classification system is important to group and classify the millions of living organisms. This system is periodically modified based on the consensus of several scientists at an international level.

The current classification system can be summarized as below and shown in a concept map below.
Domain → Kingdom → Phylum → Class → Order → Family → Genus → Species → Varieties/Ecotypes

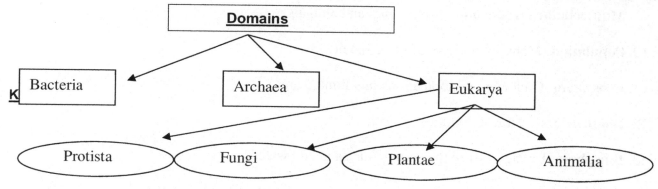

<u>**Domains**</u>

1. **Bacteria:** Most diverse group of unicellular bacteria which are called prokaryotes. Pro refers to prior to and karyon refers to nucleus. These organisms have formed before the evolution of nucleus.
2. **Archaea:** Archaebacteria. It is prokaryotic but has some parts of eukaryotic cells- They survive in extreme conditions.
3. **Eukarya:** Eu refers to truly, and karyon refers to nucleated cells. There are the cells with a true membrane bound nucleus.

> <u>**Eukaryotic Kingdoms:**</u>
> - **Protista:** Includes predominantly unicellular eukaryotes, that are heterotrophic such as paramecium, and amoeba or phototrophic such as algae and diatoms. In addition, it also includes multicellular organisms such as Kelp.
> - **Fungi:** Mostly there are multicellular and some are unicellular organisms. All fungi are heterotrophic. e.g. yeast.
> - **Plantae:** Includes all higher plants which are flowering plants (angiosperms) and non-flowering plants (gymnosperms). The flowering plants include the broad groups of Monocots and dicot plants. All plants are photoautotrophs.
> - **Animalia:** includes all animals. These are multicellular and heterotrophic.

V. BIOLOGICAL HIERARCHY

All things living and non-living are made up of atoms and molecules. Even the most complex organisms are built from basic elements and molecules. The living world has a hierarchical order as shown below and we study them at different levels in different experiments.

1. **Atoms** (C, H, O, N, S)

2. **Molecules** (CO_2, O_2, H_2O, amino acids, simple sugars)

3. **Macromolecules** (proteins, carbohydrates, lipids)

4. **Parts of cells** (membrane and organelles such as nucleus & mitochondria)

5. **Cells** (unicellular organisms and cells of multicellular organisms)

6. **Tissues** (bone, muscle, nerve tissue)

7. **Organs** (heart, lungs, brain)

8. **Organ systems** (circulatory or reproductive systems)

9. **Multicellular Organisms** (plants, fungi and animals)

10. **Population** (Many individuals of same species)

11. **Ecosystem** (Collection of populations in a limited area)

12. **Biomes** (Desert, forest, tundra)

13. **Biosphere** (Living crust of the earth in air, land and water).

2. CHEMISTRY FOR BIOLOGY

Concepts
1. While protons define the elements, neutrons define the isotopes and electrons determine the chemical and physical properties of atoms.
2. Atoms combine to make molecules through covalent bonds, ionic bonds and hydrogen bonds.
3. Molecules vary in their polarity due to the differences in electronegativity of the atoms involved and may contribute to the above bonds and interactions.
4. Polarity of water and hydrogen bonding between water molecules result in many properties of water such as cohesiveness and high specific heat that are essential to support life.
5. Water is a major component of living organisms and participates in many essential biochemical reactions.
6. Concentration of hydrogen ions, as measured by pH, affects the properties of biological molecules and influences the biochemical reactions.
7. Organic compounds based on their structure and functional groups attached to them vary in their size, shape and properties.

Outline
I.   Atoms and Molecules
II. Water and Aqueous Solutions
III. Carbon Compounds

I. ATOMS AND MOLECULES

All things great and small, living and non-living, are made of simple atoms and molecules. In this chapter we will look at some basic terms related to this subject and the different types of bonds and interactions between atoms and molecules.

I.   Basic Definitions and Concepts

Matter: A substance that takes up space and has mass.
Element: A substance made up of a single atom. It cannot be broken down to other substances by ordinary chemical means. Elements are defined by the number of protons they have.
Compound: Two or more different elements combined.
Molecule: Two or more atoms bonded together.
Atom: The unit of a matter. Atoms consist of 3 major particles. Proton is a positively charged particle and has mass of 1 atomic mass unit (amu) or Dalton (Da). Neutron is an uncharged particle and has a mass of 1 amu or Da. Electrons are negatively charged and has 1/1000ᵗʰ of amu or Da.

The combined mass of protons and neutrons is the **mass number** (approximate mass) or the **atomic weight** (the absolute weight with reference to H or O, and it is the average of isotopic weights of an element). The number of protons in each element is unique, and it is called the **atomic number**.

Living organisms contain about 25 elements. The 4 major elements that make up about 96 % of the living matter are C, O, H and N. The elements P, S, Ca and K make up about 3-4%. Other essential elements for life such as iron, magnesium and iodine are needed in small amounts and are called trace elements.

Isotopes of an element contain the same number of protons but varying number of neutrons. For example,
^{12}C = 6 protons + 6 neutrons   - a stable isotope
^{13}C = 6 protons + 7 neutrons   - a stable isotope
^{14}C = 6 protons + 8 neutrons   - a radioactive isotope

Stable isotopes can also be used for biological experiments when special methods can be used to separate molecules based on their atomic weights. Radioisotopes emit radiation due to the unstable nucleus. Some of the radioisotopes are used in biological experiments to determine the age of a fossil or detect DNA and RNA. For example, ^{14}C has a half life ($t_{1/2}$; the time it takes for the element to lose half of its original mass) of 5,730 years. It is used for carbon dating and incorporation of carbon into various biological molecules. Stable isotopes emit no radiation. For example, ^{14}N and ^{15}N are used in labeling DNA and in mass spectroscopy.

Valence electrons are the electrons in the outermost orbit, which interact with other atoms. By analogy, if the nucleus is the size of a football, the electrons will be spinning a few miles away from it. The nuclei of two atoms never contact each other. Thus, all interactions in chemical bonds and in chemical reactions are between electrons only. The only time a proton interacts with other atoms is in a simple hydrogen (H) atom, which is made of an electron and a proton. When H loses the electron, the proton (H^+) can interact with the surrounding atoms.

Valence of an atom refers to its bonding capacity and is determined by its unpaired valence electrons. If there are 4 valence electrons (for example, carbon), it can make 4 covalent bonds and its valence is 4. If there are 5 valence electrons, it can make three bonds and its valence is 3; if it is 6, the valence is two, and if it is 7, the valence is 1. If the valence electrons are 3 or less, they tend to lose their electrons to their partners, as you can see in ionic bonding below due to the stronger and more electronegative atom completely pulling the electrons to its valence shell. For example, the valence of H = 1, O = 2, N = 3, C = 4 and so on.

Octet rule: An atom (in the second or third row of periodic Table) needs 2 electrons in its first shell and 8 electrons in the 2nd or the third orbits to complete the valence shell. If it is complete, it is inert. If not, they are reactive to interact and bond with other atoms to complete their valence shell. For example, helium, neon and argon are inert gases with 2 electrons in their first shell (He) and 8 each in their 2nd (Ne) and 3rd shells (Ar).

Electronegativity: It refers to the relative ability of an atom to attract electrons when it is combined with another atom; the stronger the electronegativity of an atom, the greater its affinity for the electrons from other atoms. The electronegativity depends on the number of valence electrons and the size of the atom. The top right corner in the Periodic Table consists of atoms with high electronegativity values. For example, fluorine has the highest value (4.0) followed by oxygen (3.5) compared to the lower values of carbon (3.5), sodium (1.0) and hydrogen (2.1). This feature of an atom tends to form ionic bonds and also leads to the formation of cations (+) and anions (-). See ionic bonding later in this chapter.

II. Chemical Bonds and Interactions
1. **Covalent bonding:** Two atoms share a pair of electrons. This is the strongest of all bonds (~ 50 - 170 kcal/mol), present in all compounds and molecules. Specifically, the glycosidic bonds of carbohydrates, ester bonds of lipids, peptide bonds of proteins, and phosphodiester bonds of DNA/RNA are all examples of covalent bonds.

There are two kinds of covalent bonds:
a. *Non-polar covalent bonding* occurs when two atoms, with same or similar electronegativity, and the atoms in these molecules share electrons equally. Examples are H_2, O_2, CO_2, CH_4, C_2H_6 and C_3H_8.

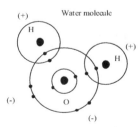

b. *Polar covalent bonding* occurs when two atoms share electrons unequally, e.g., H_2O (see Figure in the next page), NH_3. One of the atoms (such as O and N) is strongly electronegative than the other (H). The electrons spin around the strongly electronegative atoms more than the weakly electronegative atoms resulting in a partial positive charges and partial negative charges. In addition, there are unpaired electrons in the case of oxygen in water resulting in partial negative charges.

Nonpolar and Polar Covalent Bonds

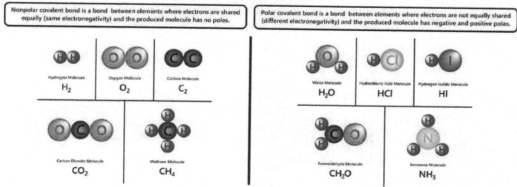

2. **Ionic bonds:** When the electronegativity of one atom is greater than that of the adjoining atom, the one with higher electronegativity pulls electrons to its valence shell from its neighboring atom, thereby becoming an anion (with a negative charge). The other atom becomes a cation (positive charge) after losing an electron. This generates ionic bonding due to the attraction of + and - charges (~3-7 kcal/mol).

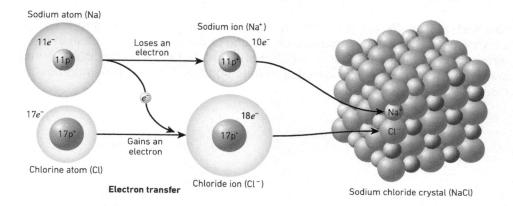

In biological context, the ionic bonds are weaker than covalent bonds, as they are found in low concentrations under aqueous surroundings. For example, in NaCl, Sodium (Na) has 11 electrons with one electron in its valence shell, and chlorine has a total of 17 electrons with 7 electrons in the valence shell. Chlorine gains the single valence electron from Na and becomes a chloride (Cl^-) ion (anion with negative charge), and sodium becomes a Na^+ ion (cation with positive charge). Ionic bonds can be found in proteins between positively and negatively charged amino acids.

3. **H-bonding:** The hydrogen covalently attached to one electronegative atom is attracted to another electronegative atom. This attraction is called H-bonding; H- bonds (~3-7 kcal/mol) are similar to ionic bonds but stronger than van der Waals interactions or hydrophilic interactions. Examples include attraction between water molecules, H-bonds between H_2O and NH_3, and the H-bonds of DNA, RNA and proteins. The H-bonds in water is shown below.

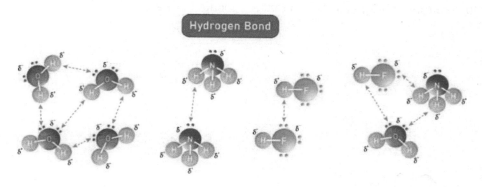

Hydrogen Bond

4. **Hydrophilic and Hydrophobic interactions:** Hydrophilic (water-loving) substances are normally polar, charged molecules, soluble in water. Hydrophobic (water-fearing) molecules are normally non-polar, lipid-soluble molecules that are excluded from aqueous solutions by hydrogen bonding among polar molecules.

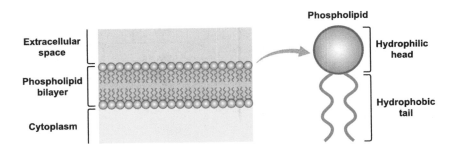

Example: The phospholipids in biological membranes have the hydrophilic region outside the membrane bilayer to interact with aqueous environment and hydrophobic region inside the membrane bilayer. Amino acids with hydrophobic side chains tend to be in the interior portion of proteins while the amino acids with hydrophilic side chains can be either in the interior or exterior portion.

5. **Van der Waals interaction:** When the atoms in a closely packed molecules interact, there are pockets of constantly changing positive and negative charges due to the changing distribution of electron clouds. These temporary charges, though small (~1 kcal/mol), contribute to van der Waals interactions within such polar and non-polar molecules. Examples include lipids in biological membranes and cellulose in plant cell walls.

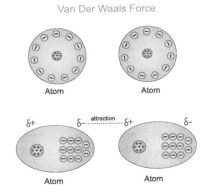

Summary
Covalent bonds are formed by sharing the electrons equally (non-polar) or unequally (polar). Ionic bonds are formed by one atom losing an electron to another atom resulting in a positively charged cations and negatively charged anions. Hydrogen bonds are formed due to dipole attraction of a partially and positively charged hydrogen and a partially and negatively charged oxygen or nitrogen. Hydrophilic attractions and hydrophobic repulsions are due to polar and non-polar molecules interacting with water respectively. Van der Waals forces are weak attractions between a constantly changing positive (due to protons) and negative (due to electrons) charges in atoms that are located closely.

II. WATER AND AQUEOUS SOLUTIONS

Water is essential for life as living organisms are made of up to 95 % water. In addition, it is the medium and an important ingredient for many biochemical reactions. In this chapter, we will look at the properties of water and water based (aqueous) solutions.

I Water and H-bonding
Hydrogen and oxygen share the electrons unequally resulting in partial positive and partial negative charges on hydrogen and oxygen, respectively. A single water molecule is tetrahedral in shape. The two electron orbitals of oxygen and two of hydrogen make the four corners of the tetrahedral structure of the water molecule.

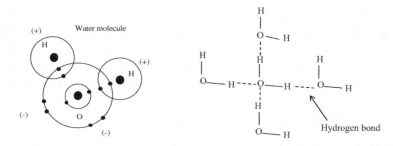

Because of the two partial positive and negative charges, water molecules can H-bond with up to 4 other water molecules. The relatively strong H-bonding in water is the main reason for its unique properties.

Properties of Water

1. <u>Cohesiveness</u> due to constant forming and breaking of H-bonds in liquid water. This is important for water uptake (transport from roots to leaves and other parts of the plant) and imbibition (water intake) by seeds by absorption. Adherence of water to the surface of other objects is referred to adhesiveness. This is also important for the attachment of water (adsorption) which may result in absorption.

2. <u>High specific heat.</u> The specific heat of water is 1 cal/g/^{O}C compared to 0.1 cal/g/^{O}C for iron and 0.6 cal/g/^{O}C for ethanol. Water can absorb and release heat to stabilize the temperature in the surrounding area to make it habitable.

3. <u>High heat of vaporization.</u> It takes 540 cal to evaporate 1 g of water compared to 237 cal/g for ethanol and 59 cal/g for chloroform. This helps in evaporative cooling for both animals and plants during the hot weather.

4. <u>Freezing and expansion.</u> Water is densest at 4°C and it expands during freezing. The H-bonds between water molecules in ice keep each molecule farther apart from one other compared to liquid water. Since ice is lighter than water, it floats on the surface to keep the water below warmer, thus providing a favorable environment for aquatic organisms to live under cold conditions.

5. <u>Versatile solvent</u> for all polar and charged molecules. Water is an excellent solvent because of its polarity. Minerals and other nutrients dissolved in water are available for easy uptake and transport by plants and animals.

6. <u>Medium and an ingredient for many biochemical reactions.</u> Living cells contain up to 95% water, and all biochemical reactions in a cell occur under aqueous conditions. Many biochemical reactions need water as a reactant and some reactions produce water as a byproduct. For example, photosynthesis utilizes water to extract electrons to fix carbon dioxide to make carbohydrates. Without water and photosynthesis, there would be no organic molecules made in nature other than the limited amount of chemosynthesis in

bacteria. This is the most essential property of water to support life.

IV. Aqueous Solutions

Water based (aqueous) solutions have two major properties: solute concentration and H^+ ion concentration. A solute is the substance completely dissolved in a solvent.

1. Solute concentration: The solute concentration can be measured in molarity, weight/volume, % of solid per unit volume, ppm, ppb etc. For example, a solution may have 0.5M sucrose, blood cholesterol may be measured as 200mg/dL and you may purchase milk with 2% fat (2g per 100ml of milk). Molar concentrations are the most commonly used units in scientific experiments.

Molecular weight (MW) is the sum of the weight of all the atoms in a molecule. Sometimes the formula weight (FW) is used to refer to the MW of a chemical formulation. MW is expressed in Daltons.
For example, MW of NaOH = 23 (Na) + 16 (O) + 1 (H) = 40.

Mole: Mole refers to the MW expressed in grams for practical purposes of dealing with two different solutes containing an equivalent number of molecules. It is based on the Avogadro's number that one mole of any substance contains 6.023×10^{23} molecules. For example, 1 mole of NaOH (40 g) contains the same number of molecules as 1 mole of sucrose (342g) or 1 mole of any other substance. This concept helps us measure the accurate concentration of several atoms and molecules in a given solution.

Molarity (M): It is one mole of a solute dissolved in one liter of a solution. One molar concentration refers to one gram-mole of a substance dissolved in one-liter solution. For example, 1 M of NaOH means 40g of NaOH are dissolved in a liter of this solution. To make 0.1 M, you need to have 4 g NaOH in a liter of solution.

This is an important concept to understand for doing experiments in the biological laboratory. The fractions of molarity are expressed as follows.

1×10^{-3} M = 1mM   (millimolar)
1×10^{-6} M = 1µM   (micromolar)
1×10^{-9} M = 1nM   (nanomolar)
1×10^{-12} M = 1pM   (picomolar)
1×10^{-15} M = 1fM   (femtomolar)

Making molar solutions
This section gives some general idea of how you can make molar solutions from solid or from another solution.

    From solid to solution: Use the formula
MW or FW (g/mole) x M (mole/L) x liters (L).
If the units are not in molarity (M) or liters (L), then you need to convert the given unit to M and liters.
For example, to make 100 ml of 0.5 M NaOH (MW = 40):
40 g/mole x 0.5 mole/liter x 100 ml x 1 liter/1000 ml = 2 g

    From stock (solution 1) to a diluted (solution 2):
Use the formula   **C1.V1 = C2.V2**   Where,
C1 is the concentration of stock solution 1.
C2 is the concentration of working solution 2.
V1 is the volume of stock solution you need to calculate.
V2 is the volume of the working solution to be made.

You can use any units in this formula but make sure that the units are same on both sides of the equations.
For example, to make 100 ml of 2 % NaCl from 10 % NaCl,
You will set up the formula as 10 % V1 = 2 % x 100 ml
Solve this to get 20 ml of stock solution, and the reminder (100 ml – 20 ml = 80 ml) will be water.

2. Hydrogen ion concentration [H+]: Acids, Bases and Buffers

In pure water, approximately one in 554 million molecules is ionized (dissociated) into H^+ and OH^- (hydroxide) ions. The concentration of H^+, expressed as $[H^+]$, is equal to that of OH^-. At equilibrium, $[H^+]$ = $[OH^-]$.

We can measure the $[H^+]$ in water or water-based solutions by using the concept of pH.

The **pH** of a solution is a measure of the negative logarithm of its H^+ ion concentration = $-\log_{10}[H^+]$. The negative log is used to simplify the molarity into simple numbers of pH. For an aqueous solution, pH varies from 1 to 14. For practical purposes, this is the range between minimum and maximum pH.

In any aqueous solution, the K_w (water constant) will be the product of $[H^+]$ and $[OH^-]$; $K_w = [H^+] \times [OH^-]$ and in pure water, it is 10^{-7} M $\times$ 10^{-7} M = 10^{-14} M.

So, in an aqueous solution, the changes in $[H^+]$ and $[OH^-]$ in various pH is shown in the Table below.

pH	$[H^+]$	$[OH^-]$	Kw
5	10^{-5}M	10^{-9}M	10^{-14}
6	10^{-6}M	10^{-8}M	10^{-14}
7	10^{-7}M	10^{-7}M	10^{-14}
8	10^{-8}M	10^{-6}M	10^{-14}
9	10^{-9}M	10^{-5}M	10^{-14}

Remember that as the pH increases, the $[H^+]$ decreases and the $[OH^-]$ increases. Also, note that when pH changes by one unit the $[H^+]$ or $[OH^-]$ changes 10-fold because the pH units are logarithmic. For example, a solution with a pH of 4 has 100 times more $[H^+]$ than a solution with a pH of 6.

Acid is a chemical that dissociates in a solution and increases the $[H^+]$. As a result, it can be considered as a proton (H^+) donor that increases $[H^+]$ in a solution, e.g., $HCl \rightarrow H^+ + Cl^-$.

Base is a chemical that is either a proton acceptor or hydroxide donor that can decrease $[H^+]$ or increase $[OH^-]$ in a solution, e.g., $NH_3 + H^+ \rightarrow NH_4^+$

$\quad NaOH \rightarrow Na^+ + OH^-$ and then $OH^- + H^+ \rightarrow H_2O$

Aqueous solutions at pH 7 are called neutral, below 7 as acidic and above 7 as basic, e.g., stomach acid pH = 2, blood pH = 7.4, bleach pH = 12.5.

Buffer is a substance that minimizes the pH change by accepting excess H^+s, when pH decreases or by donating H^+, when pH increases. Most buffers are weak acids or weak bases.

Buffering range and pK

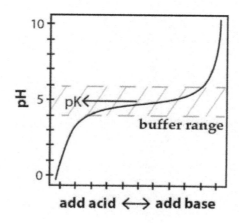

add acid $\longleftrightarrow$ add base

The **pK** is the pH at which the ratio of an acid form to the base form is one. For example, in the above case, at a particular pH, the concentration of carbonic acid (H_2CO_3) is the same as that of bicarbonate (HCO_3^-). That pH (6.6) will be the pK for this buffer system. The buffer has the greatest capacity to maintain the pH of an aqueous solution around its pK value, e.g., Trizma buffer has a pK value of 8.1 and it is used for many DNA experiments, when the optimum pH needed is from 7 to 9, the buffering range of Trizma. There are acidic-, neutral- or basic- buffers with a pK in that respective range. Depending on the experimental system, you can choose the best buffer you can find.

Amino acids can act as a buffer by donating or accepting protons depending on the pH increase or decrease respectively as shown below. Under neutral pH, amino acids have both positive and negative charges due to this.

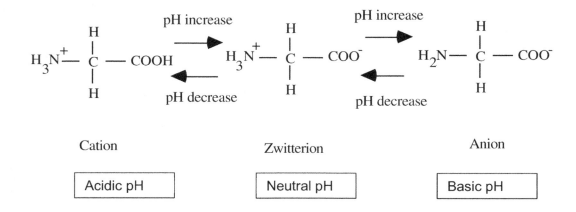

Cation   Zwitterion   Anion

Acidic pH   Neutral pH   Basic pH

III. CARBON COMPOUNDS

Carbon Compounds, Isomers and Functional Groups

Next to water, organic molecules (carbon based) are the major components in living systems. Carbon, hydrogen, nitrogen and oxygen, phosphorus and sulfur are the major elements in living organisms and are present in similar percentages in the living organisms. All the biological molecules are organic compounds of vast diversity. Simple organic compounds are hydrocarbons such as methane (CH_4) and ethane (CH_3-CH_3) which may contain few carbons.

Complex organic molecules include large molecules (macromolecules such as proteins, polysaccharides, DNA and RNA) which may have millions of carbons connected together. Organic compounds may be linear (aliphatic, e.g., glycerol), branched (isoleucine) or circular (aromatic, e.g., phenol and cholesterol), saturated (no double bonds between carbons, e.g., palmitic acid) or unsaturated (one or more double bonds between carbons, e.g., oleic acid). Organic molecules are represented by molecular formula (e.g., CH_4) and structural formula.

Sometimes, chemical structures are abbreviated with just lines. For example, cyclohexane (C_6H_{12}) can be represented by a hexagon.

Or a $CH_3CH_2CH_2CH_2CH_3$ can be represented by a wiggly line.

Whenever there is an oxygen or nitrogen in a carbon ring, it is written out but the carbons are not.

ISOMERS

Isomers are organic molecules with the same molecular formula and different structural formulae and different properties. They occur in three different types: structural, geometric and optical isomers.

1. <u>Structural isomers</u> have the same molecular formula but different structures, e.g., leucine and isoleucine. This results in two different molecules, though they contain same number and type of atoms.

2. <u>Geometric isomers</u> form due to the inflexibility of double bonds between the carbons. If the same types of functional groups are on the same side, they are called cis configuration, and if they are away from each other, it is called trans configuration. Examples are the cis-fat and trans-fat.

3. <u>Optical isomers or enantiomers</u>: These are mirror images of each other. Optical isomers occur when a carbon is attached asymmetrically to 4 different atoms or molecules, e.g., L-amino acid (L = laevus-left handed - used by cells) and D-amino acid (D = dexter, right handed - rarely used and may be toxic to cells).

The 3-dimenstional shape and the nature of functional groups of each molecule determine its biological activity and usefulness. The functional groups are explained in next section.

FUNCTIONAL GROUPS

Functional groups are atoms or groups of atoms, covalently bonded to the carbon skeleton. The functional groups greatly influence the property and reactivity of the organic molecule to which they are attached, based on their number and position.

1. Hydroxyl group (-OH): Since oxygen is electronegative and hydrogen is slightly positive, the -OH group confers polarity to the molecule. It makes the molecule easily soluble in water. Molecules with hydroxyl group(s) are generally called alcohols. Almost all carbohydrates, proteins and nucleic acids contain -OH groups, e.g., sugars and alcohols.

2. Carbonyl group (-C=O): This is also a polar functional group. Organic solvents such as propanal and acetone contain -C=O groups. If it is at the end of an organic molecule, it is an aldehyde, e.g., glucose. If it is in the middle, the molecule is a ketone, e.g., fructose. Carbonyl groups are present in simple sugars, some proteins and nucleotides. A carbonyl group in simple sugars may react with an -OH group to form a ring structure.

3. Carboxyl group (-COOH): It is an acidic group. It can ionize to form -the conjugate base, COO^- and releases H^+ to increase $[H^+]$ of the solution or decrease pH, e.g., acetic acid, formic acid, citric acid and malic acid. Ionized forms are called acetate, formate, citrate and malate, respectively. The -COOH group is also present in all amino acids, fatty acids and proteins.

4. Amino group (-NH$_2$): Amines act as a base by accepting protons ($-NH_2 + H^+ = -NH_3^+$). An amino group is found in all amino acids, proteins and some specific nucleotides. Amino group ionizes at the neutral cellular pH to become $-NH_3^+$.

5. Sulfhydryl group (-SH): This is a reactive group. An -SH group is present in the amino acid, cysteine. Two such -SH groups within a protein can combine to make a disulfide bridge (-S-S-) to stabilize a protein structure. -SH groups are sometimes found in active sites being involved in the catalysis of enzymes.

14

6. **Phosphate group** (-OPO_3^{2-}): This is important in high energy compounds such as adenosine triphosphate (ATP). Phosphate group is the conjugate base of the phosphoric acid (H_3PO_4). It is ionized at the neutral cellular pH. It is also, present in DNA, RNA strands and in all other nucleotides. Phosphate is found in phospholipids. Pi refers to inorganic phosphates and PPi refers to pyrophosphate. This is an acidic and a reactive group.

7. **Methyl group** (-CH_3): It is a non-polar functional group. It affects the solubility of a compound in aqueous or organic solutions. It has a strong influence on the bioactivity of the molecule involved. Methylation (adding a methyl group) of a DNA molecule can make it non-functional. Methylation of some drugs or pesticides makes them more permeable through cell membranes. Methyl groups are found in alcohols, fatty acids, some amino acids and nucleotides.

Remember and try to identify these functional groups in biological molecules. They are important to recognize as they will help one to understand the properties of these molecules.

Summary of Functional Groups

Functional Group	Molecular formula	Properties	Examples
Hydroxyl	-OH	Alcohol	Simple sugars, glycerol, ethanol
Carbonyl	-C=O	Aldehyde (end) Ketone (middle)	Simple sugars in their linear form; aldose and ketose
Carboxyl	-COOH or -COO$^-$	Acid or conjugate base	Amino acids and fatty acids
Amine	-NH$_2$ or -N$^+$H$_3$	Base or conjugate acid	Amino acid, nitrogenous base
Phosphate	-PO$_4{}^{2-}$	Acid and conjugate base	Phospholipids and Nucleotides such as nucleoside triphosphates (NTPs)
Sulfhydryl	-SH	Thiols	Beta mercaptoethanol and the amino acid – cystine
Methyl or hydrocarbons	-CH$_3$ -CH$_2$	No special name	All hydrocarbons contain -CH$_2$ or -CH$_3$.

3. BIOLOGICAL MOLECULES

Concepts

1. Several subunit molecules are used to synthesize each class of biological molecules.
2. Condensation/dehydration reactions are used for the synthesis of biological molecules in cells while hydrolysis reactions break down biological molecules.
3. A simple monosaccharide like glucose can be used to construct many chemically distinct oligosaccharides and polysaccharides.
4. Lipids are a class of biological molecules not classified as polymers. They are generally non-polar and form a wide variety of molecules.
5. Phospholipids are amphipathic molecules that form the main structure of biological membranes.
6. The structure of a fatty acid's hydrocarbon chain determines its properties and the properties and functions of the phospholipids and triglycerides made from it.
7. Proteins are made of amino acids which interact with each other as the polypeptide folds.
8. The overall 3-D shape of a protein is important for its optimal function and it is formed by several bonds and interactions at multiple levels.
9. When a globular protein folds in an aqueous solution, the hydrophilic R groups generally tend to be exposed on the surface of this protein while the hydrophobic R groups generally tend to be concealed inside.
10. Denaturation causes a protein to unfold, making it nonfunctional.
11. Nucleic acids (DNA and RNA) are polymers made of nucleotide monomers.
12. The DNA double helix is formed by complementary base pairing and RNA forms variable secondary structures.

Outline

Condensation Synthesis and Hydrolysis
I. Carbohydrates
II. Lipids
III. Proteins
IV. Nucleic Acids

Condensation Synthesis and Hydrolysis

As we discussed biological hierarchy in the first chapter, atoms combine to form molecules that are used to build macromolecules such as DNA, RNA, proteins, carbohydrates and lipids, all of which form the building blocks of life. The four major groups of biological molecules are carbohydrates, lipids, proteins and nucleic acids. Each part of the cell is composed of several different types of biological molecules. Some of the biological molecules are small and they are used as monomers to make larger molecules. Some are very large (1000s of Daltons) and are called as macromolecules. The size limit for macromolecules is an arbitrary one. Simple sugars, amino acids, nucleotides and almost all lipids are relatively very small compared to the macromolecules such as polysaccharides, polypeptides, DNA and RNA.

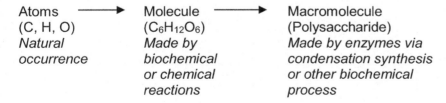

Atoms $\longrightarrow$ Molecule $\longrightarrow$ Macromolecule
(C, H, O) $(C_6H_{12}O_6)$ (Polysaccharide)
Natural   *Made by*   *Made by enzymes via*
occurrence   *biochemical*   *condensation synthesis*
             or chemical   *or other biochemical*
             reactions   *process*

Condensation synthesis: The individual units that make a large molecule are called monomers. Monomers typically contain –H and –OH groups attached to them. Two monomers are combined in a condensation reaction to make a dimer by the removal of an -H and an -OH group, which condense to form a water (H_2O) molecule. More monomers are added in a similar reaction to synthesize polymers.

Condensation synthesis of a macromolecule is performed by a specific enzyme that uses specific monomers to make that polymer. The condensation synthesis process creates bonds between the monomers in carbohydrates, lipids, and proteins. Nucleic acids are polymerized by a nucleophilic attack, but the reaction is similar to condensation synthesis. An older terminology refers to condensation synthesis as "dehydration synthesis" but it is not accurate description as the cells do not lose water, they instead form water.

Hydrolysis: It breaks down dimers, trimers or polymers into monomers by adding an -H and an -OH group derived from the splitting of a water molecule (hydrolysis).

This is important for catabolic processes that utilize the energy stored in different macromolecules. Hydrolysis of a macromolecule is performed by a specific enzyme, e.g., cellulose is degraded by cellulase and DNA is degraded by DNase. Almost all enzymes are proteins catalyzing a reaction. Their names usually end with the suffix "ase" except when 'ase' is preceded by capital 'A'. In such a situation, the capital 'A' is deleted, e.g., DNAase changes to DNase.

To summarize, condensation synthesis makes polymer containing n monomers and releases n-1 water. Hydrolysis utilizes n-1 water to break down a polymer made of n monomers to release the monomers. Since water is involved, it is referred to as "hydro"-lysis (break down)

I. CARBOHYDRATES

Monosaccharides
These simple sugars are the monomers (single units) that make up complex carbohydrates with many units.
- Simple sugars are made of C, H and O in a ratio of C:H_2:O
- Produced by photosynthetic organisms

$$CO_2 + H_2O + light \text{----------}> CH_2O + O_2$$

- The carbon skeleton size varies from 3 to 7 carbons

- An -OH group is attached to each C, except for one which is double bonded to an O (carbonyl-CO). If -CO is at the end, it is an aldose sugar, e.g., glucose, if -CO is in the middle, it is a ketose sugar, e.g., fructose.
- In aqueous solutions, the sugars with 5-7 carbons form a ring structure.

Glyceraldehyde **Dihydroxyacetone**

Ribose **Glucose**

A hexose such as glucose, forms a ring structure with the -C=O group in the first carbon bonding with the -OH group in the fifth carbon. When such ring structures form, if the -OH group on first C is below the plane of the ring, it is a alpha-glucose and if it is above the plane, it is a beta-glucose.

Functions
- Major source of energy for cells, e.g., glucose and fructose
- Energy stored in chemical bonds of sugars is harvested by cells through respiration.
- Carbon skeletons are used for making other molecules.

Disaccharides
These are formed by enzymes through condensation synthesis to combine two monosaccharides through glycosidic linkages and forms water.

Disaccharide

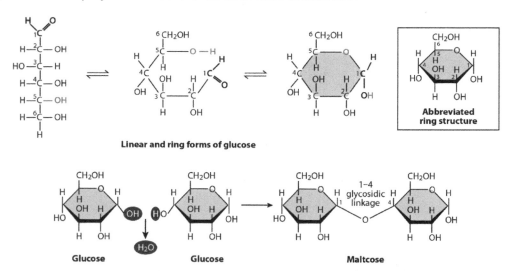

	Sucrose Glucose and Fructose
	Lactose Galactose and Glucose
	Maltose Glucose and Glucose

Alpha and beta linkages

The two different glycosidic linkages are named based on the position of the -OH group attached to the first C of the monosaccharide. As we saw earlier, if the -OH group is below the plane of sugars, it is an alpha-linkage, and if it is above the plane, it is a beta-linkage. The positioning of the -OH group in such linkages occurs during the cyclization (ring formation) of monosaccharides and the selection of a particular monosaccharide by the specific enzyme involved in disaccharide biosynthesis. These linkages determine the properties of the resulting carbohydrates. Numbers in alpha-1, 4 or beta-1, 4 indicate the linkages between the first C of monosaccharide-1 and the 4th C of monosaccharide-2. The type of linkage is critical in deciding whether the polymer will be broken down into monomers.

Linear and ring forms of glucose

Abbreviated ring structure

Dehydration reaction in the synthesis of maltose.

Glucose   Glucose   Maltose

Polysaccharides

Polysaccharides are long chains of carbohydrates with several thousands of monomers. Shorter chains of carbohydrates are called oligosaccharides (~ 5 to 20 sugar molecules).

Polysaccharides can be grouped into storage and structural forms based on their structure and function. Storage carbohydrates are used for energy utilization and structural ones are used to build cell walls and exoskeletons.

Examples of **storage polysaccharides** are given below.

1. Starch: alpha-1,4 linked glucose, amylose and amylopectin in plants. They are the major storage products in potato, rice, wheat and corn.
2. Glycogen: similar to starch but highly branched alpha1, 4 linked polysaccharides stored in the liver and

muscles of animals. Both starch and glycogen are easily digestible by humans as we have the enzymes to digest them.

Examples of **structural polysaccharides** are given below.
1. <u>Cellulose</u>: beta 1,4 linked glucose molecules. They are the major constituents of plant cell walls, the most abundant biopolymers on earth. Cellulose can be degraded by cellulase enzyme made by wood-rotting fungi and bacteria.
2. <u>Callose</u>: shorter than cellulose. It contains beta 1, 3 linked glucose molecules, formed at wounding sites in plants. These are relatively shorter than cellulose.
3. <u>Chitin</u>: beta 1, 4 linked N-acetyl glucosamine (NAG). It is the major structural component of exoskeletons of insects and cell walls of fungi. Chitin in fungal cell walls can be degraded by chitinase enzyme made by plants as a part of defense mechanisms against fungi.
4. Bacterial cell wall contains a modified polysaccharide called NAM-NAG (N-acetyl muramic acid and N-acetyl glucosamine).

II. LIPIDS

Features
- Highly non-polar and do not mix with water (hydrophobic)
- Soluble in organic solvents such as ether and chloroform.
- Three major kinds: fats (triglycerides), phospholipids and other lipids such as cholesterol, steroid hormones and carotenoids etc.

Functions:
- Storage of energy (9 Cal/g of fat)
- Insulation against heat loss and cushions vital organs
- Serve as vitamins, pigments, growth hormones or regulators.
- A major component of lipid bilayer of biological membranes.

Fats
Glycerol (a 3-carbon alcohol) combined with fatty acids (a long hydrocarbon chain with a -COOH group) makes up fat, which may be mono-, di-, or triglyceride, depending on the number of fatty acids it contains. For example, glycerol + 3 fatty acids = triglyceride. Depending upon whether one or two fatty acids are combined with a glycerol, they are called mono- or diglycerides respectively.

Condensation synthesis of monoglyceride

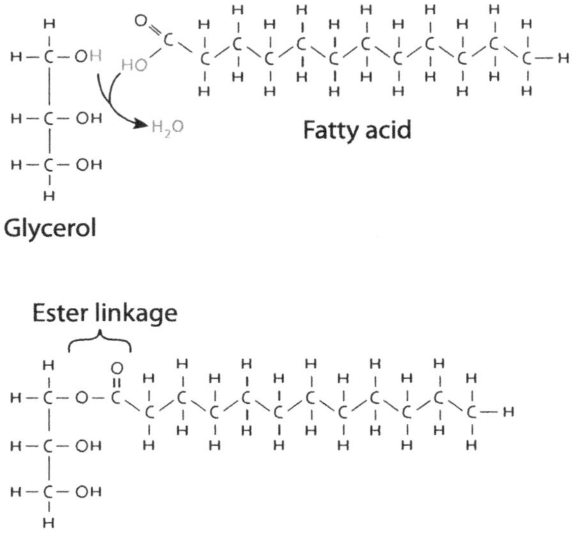

Glycerol   Fatty acid

Ester linkage

Fat molecule (monoglyceride)

The fatty acids in fats may be saturated (with hydrogen in all carbons) or unsaturated (with double bonds in the hydrocarbon chain). If there is a single double bond, it is mono unsaturated and if there are 2 or more double bonds, it is called polyunsaturated.

Greater the saturation level of the hydrocarbon, higher is the T_m (melting temperature) of the fat. The tropical plants tend to have more saturated fats in their membrane lipids and the temperate weather plants tend to have more unsaturated fats in their membrane lipids to provide optimal fluidity to the cell membranes.

Saturated fat	Unsaturated fat
1. Fatty acid carbon chain is saturated with H.	- Not saturated with H.
2. No double bonds or kinks bonds between carbons.	- One or more double bonds
3. Usually solid at room temp.	- Liquid at room temp.

4. Closely packed to each other   - Not so closely packed.
5. Most animal fats and   - Most plant fats, especially
        tropical oils.   temperate plant oils,
          Example: palm oil   Example: canola oil.

Phospholipids Glycerol + 2 fatty acids + a phosphate group + another chemical group (serine, choline etc.) make up phospholipids. Phospholipids have both hydrophilic and hydrophobic nature (amphipathic) due to the presence of the phosphate group and fatty acids, respectively. They are major components of lipid bilayers. They separate different parts of cells and maintain the compartments of membrane bound structures.

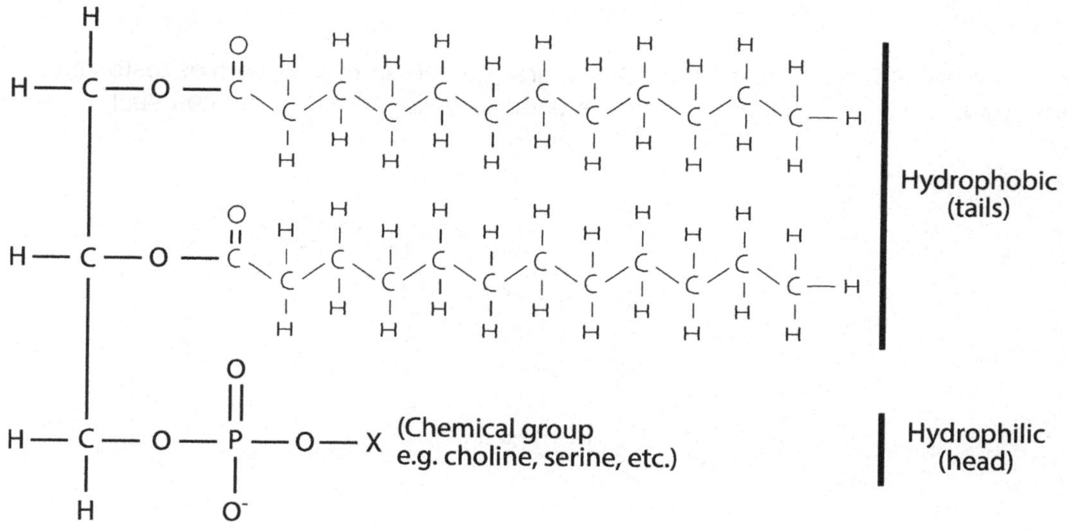

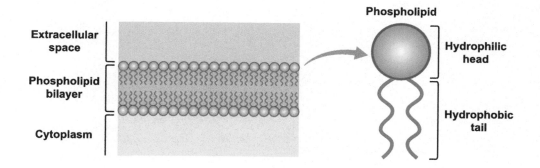

Carotenoids: The carotenoids include the color pigments used for photosynthesis in plants and precursors for vitamin-A synthesis in animals. These are made from 5-C isoprene units, e.g., beta-carotene. The Figure below illustrates carotenoids.

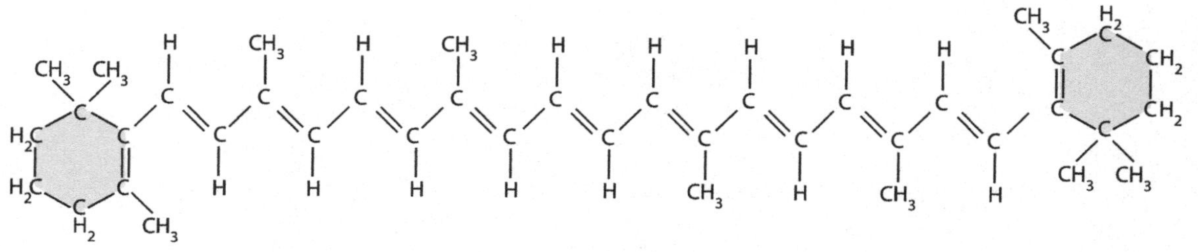

Isoprene Unit, shown on the left is a 5-C molecule used as a building block for some lipids such as carotenoids and other color pigments.

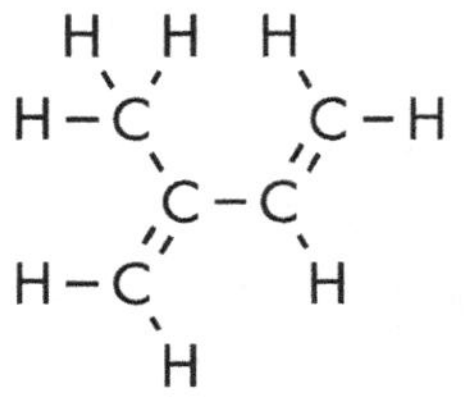

isoprene

Steroids: lipids with 4 fused C-rings, e.g., cholesterol, growth hormones such as testosterone, estradiol. The Figure below illustrates cholesterol. This is used to build steroid hormones such as estrogen and testosterone.

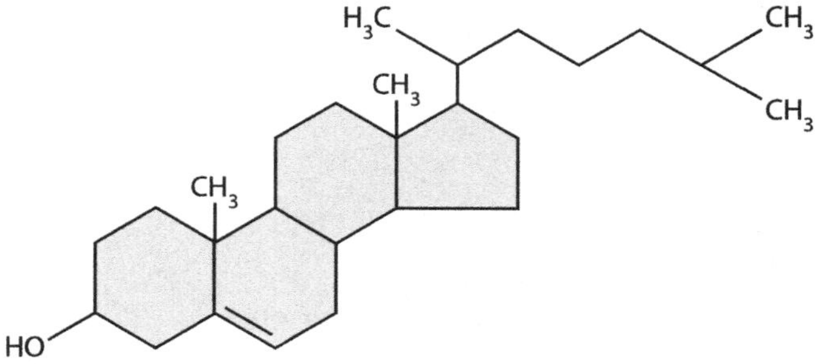

III. PROTEINS

- Made up of 20 different essential amino acids
- Structurally most diverse to suit different functions
- Major parts of living cells (~ 50 % of dry weight)

Functions	Examples
1. Structural -	keratin, collagen
2. Storage -	casein, ovalbumin
3. Transport -	ion channels, hemoglobin
4. Metabolism -	enzymes
5. Hormones -	insulin
6. Defense -	antibodies
7. Contractile -	actin, myosin
8. Signaling -	receptors
9. Movement -	microtubules, microfilaments

Amino acids are the building blocks of all proteins consisting of 20 different amino acids. All amino acids contain an amino group and a carboxylic group and they can be grouped into various classes based on the nature of their side chains as follows.

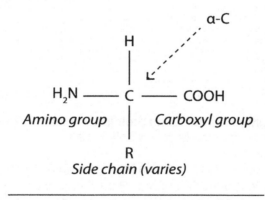

Some of the side chain characteristic and their examples are given below.

- Non-polar (hydrophobic) — glycine, alanine, valine, leucine, and isoleucine, phenylalanine, tryptophan, methionine, proline
- Polar (hydrophilic) — serine, threonine, asparagine, glutamine.
- Acidic (negative charge) — aspartic acid, glutamic acid
- Basic (positive charge) — arginine, histidine, lysine

- Linear or Aliphatic — methionine, cysteine
- Branched chain — leucine, isoleucine, valine

- Aromatic (ring) — phenylalanine, tryptophan, tyrosine
- S-containing — methionine
- -SH containing — cysteine
- -OH containing — serine, threonine, tyrosine
- Imino acid — proline

Amino Acids: Building Blocks of Life

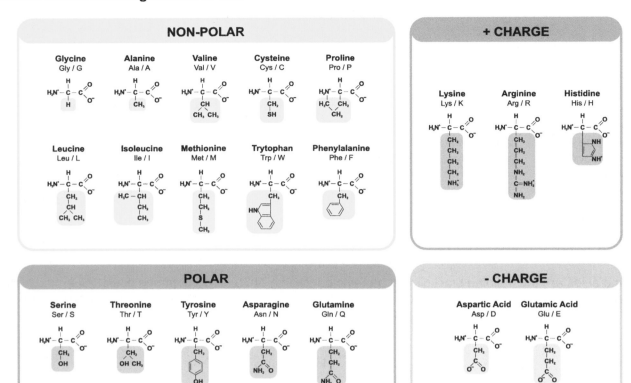

Peptide bond

The bond formed between two amino acids during protein synthesis by ribosomes is called peptide bond and a protein containing many amino acids is called polypeptide.

A peptide bond is formed by condensation synthesis by removing a H_2O molecule similar to the formation of ester bond in lipids or glycosidic bond in sugars. Peptide bonds are relatively rigid due to the C=O double bond which resonates its strength to the C-N bond making it less flexible.

Protein Structure

The three-dimensional structure of proteins is complex, elegant, and is critical for its function. It can be described at four different levels.

1. Primary structure: Amino acid sequence of a protein. The primary structure is determined by genes - the coding sequence of DNA. Since there are 20 amino acids, the possibilities of different combinations

of proteins are numerous, i.e. 20^n with n = number of amino acids in a protein. The primary structure is stabilized by peptide bonds. The amino acid sequence, i.e. its primary structure determines the higher levels of a protein's structural organization. A different sequence of amino acids will result in a different protein with possibly, a different function. Small changes in a primary structure (due to mutations in DNA) may result in a defective protein.

2. Secondary structure: Regular, repeated patterns of folding of the polypeptide, stabilized by H-bonding between the -C=O group of one amino acid and -NH group of another along the polypeptide backbone.

a. *Alpha-helix*: is one type of secondary structure wherein the -NH group of residue *n* is H-bonded to the -C=O group of residue (amino acid) n^{-4}.

Alpha-helices are found in fibrous proteins such as keratins (found in skin, claws, nails, hair and wool) and also both inside and outside of the globular proteins.

b. *B -pleated sheet*: This secondary structure is formed when H-bonding occurs between the -NH group of one strand of a protein with the -CO group of another strand of the same or different protein. The two strands may be running parallel to each other or antiparallel, e.g., silk fibers.

There are other secondary structures such as coils and loops that are less defined than the ones mentioned above.

3. Tertiary structure: It offers major contribution to the overall 3-D structure of a protein. Tertiary structure is formed due to irregular bonding between the side chains of various amino acids within a protein. Some examples are

a. *Hydrogen bonding* between two R-groups, e.g., alanine and aspartate

$-CH_2OH \longleftrightarrow {}^-OOC-CH_2-$

b. *Hydrophobic interaction* between two non-polar amino acids, e.g., alanine-alanine $-CH_3;\ _3HC-$

c. *Ionic bonding*: between an acidic and a basic amino acid. e.g., aspartate and lysine $-COO^- \text{ --- } {}^+NH_3-$

d. *Disulfide bridges:* Covalent bonding (-S-S-) between the SH groups of two cysteines. It takes two cystines to form one disulfide bond. Cys-SH + HS-Cys $\rightarrow$ Cys-S-S-Cys + H_2

4. Quaternary structure: Interaction of two or more polypeptides or subunits of multimeric proteins (i.e. contains several smaller subunits). The bonding can be a combination of ionic bonding, H-bonding, hydrophobic interaction and disulfide bridges, e.g., ☐ and ☐ subunits of hemoglobin.

Triple helix: Three separate strands of proteins are wound on each other and H-bonded to each other, e.g., collagen in cartilage. Collagens are rich in glycine, proline and hydroxy-proline. Cartilages are found under skin and in the tail of a rat.

Protein structure

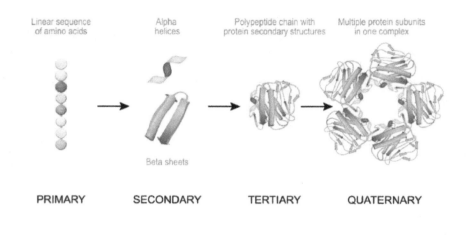

| Linear sequence of amino acids | Alpha helices | Polypeptide chain with protein secondary structures | Multiple protein subunits in one complex |

Beta sheets

PRIMARY   SECONDARY   TERTIARY   QUATERNARY

How to determine protein structure

The 3-D structures of proteins are very important in understanding their function and interaction with other components of cells or chemicals. Scientists determine protein structures through various methods including

- X-ray crystallography using crystal structures of proteins.
- Protein denaturation and renaturation studies by changing pH.
- Prediction based on known sequence and structural information.

IV. NUCLEIC ACIDS

<u>Features:</u>
- Two kinds; ribonucleic acid (RNA) and deoxyribonucleic acid (DNA).
- RNA is made of monomers called nucleotides containing a nitrogenous base + ribose + phosphate group.
- DNA is made of monomers called deoxynucleotides containing a nitrogenous base + deoxyribose + phosphate group.

<u>Functions</u>
1. Nucleotide ATP (adenosine triphosphate) is the major form of cellular energy. ATP is made of ribose + adenine + 3 inorganic phosphates.

2. Nucleotides can accept and transport electrons. NAD^+ (Nicotinamide Adenine Dinucleotide).

3. Some nucleotides serve as signal molecules, e.g., cAMP (cyclic adenosine monophosphate).

4. Hereditary; DNA molecules store genetic information, and they are replicated and passed on from generation to generation.

<u>Nucleotide</u>
Nitrogenous bases: Two kinds
      Purines: Adenine (A), guanine (G)
      Pyrimidines: Thymine (T), cytosine (C), in DNA and
                      Uracil (U)- in RNA instead of T.

Nitrogenous base + ribose sugar = nucleoside
Nitrogenous base + ribose sugar + phosphate = nucleotide.

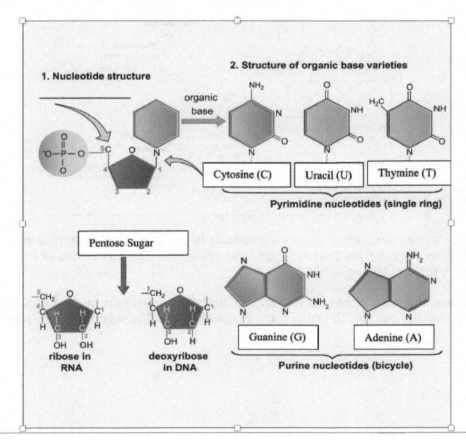

If the nucleotide has one phosphate, it is called nucleoside monophosphate (NMP); two phosphates, nucleoside diphosphate; three phosphates, nucleoside triphosphate (NTP). If the sugar is deoxy ribose as in DNA, then its monomer is called deoxyribonucleoside triphosphate (dNTP). If there are no oxygen in both 2' and 3' carbons, then it is referred to as dideoxynucleoside triphosphate (ddNTP).

Note that the 5' refers to the 5ᵗʰ carbon attached to a phosphate group and the 3' refers to the 3ʳᵈ carbon attached to the -H group.

DNA: Mostly present as double stranded with a consistent double helix structure. Base pairing between the two strands is complementary; guanine pairs with cytosine (G:C) and adenine pairs with thymine (A:T) through H-bonding. It stores genetic information in its sequence and codes for RNA. DNA is more stable than RNA because it is double stranded and it lacks 2'-OH group. The monomers used to build DNA are dNTPs namely dATP, dGTP, dCTP and dTTP.

RNA: Mostly present as single stranded with a complex and variable secondary structure. Base pairing is complementary; adenine pairs with Uracil (A:U) instead of Thymine, and Guanine pairs with Cytosine (G:C). The base pairing of RNA is also by H-bonding.
There are three major kinds of RNA:
-   mRNA (messenger)-carries information from DNA to be translated into protein,
-   rRNA (ribosomal) major part of ribosomes involved in protein synthesis,
-   tRNA (transfer) involved transferring amino acids during protein synthesis

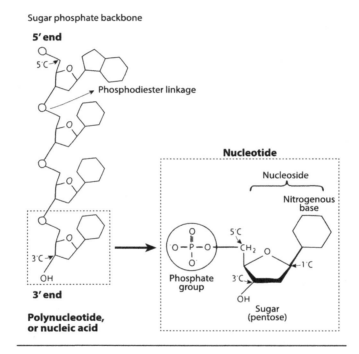

While DNA makes a fixed secondary structure of double helix, RNA on the other hand can make highly variable secondary structures based on its length and sequence. The monomers used to build RNA are NTPs namely ATP, GTP, CTP and UTP.

This chapter is very important in introductory biology and you should have a clear understanding of the various molecules and not be confused at any time about their features, functions, building blocks,

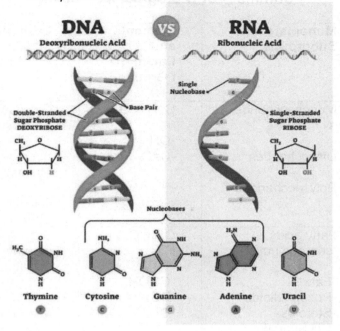

Summary of Biological Molecules

Major Group	Monomers and Subgroups	Elements and Functional Groups	Examples	Functions
Carbohydrates	Monosaccharides Disaccharides Polysaccharides	C, H & O -OH -C=O	Glucose Fructose Sucrose Maltose Cellulose Starch	Energy storage, Structure
Lipids	Fatty acids & Isoprene units -Fats -Phospholipids -Steroids -Carotenoids -Waxes	C, H, O & P -COOH, $-PO_4^{2-}$ -OH	Saturated fat: butter Unsaturated : vegetable oil Membrane lipids Cholesterol	Energy storage, Membrane structure, signal molecules
Proteins	Amino acids Structural: - Soluble - Membrane Functional: - Enzymes - Transport - Movement - Structure etc.	C, H, O, N & S $-NH_3$ -COOH -OH -SH $-CH_3$ -C=O	Soluble proteins: enzymes in the cytoplasm. Membrane proteins on plasma membrane or nuclear envelope	Energy storage, Transport, Movement, Enzyme, Immune system, Structure
Nucleic Acids	Nucleotides -DNA -RNA	C, H, O, N & P $-NH_3$ -OH $-PO_4^{2-}$ $-CH_3$	NTP: ATP, CTP, GTP UTP DNA and RNA in cells	Energy molecule (ATP, GTP) Genetic material (DNA) Making proteins (RNA)

4. ORIGIN OF LIFE

Concepts

1. Inorganic molecules possibly combined to form the building blocks to form ancestral forms or life.
2. Conditions during the early stages of earth were conducive to such formation of life.
3. RNA may possibly be the first genetic material as it can store info3rmation and catalyze reactions.

Outline
I. Origin of Life
II. Early Fossils and History of Life
III. Possible Sources of Origin
IV. RNA World
V. Classification of Current Life Forms

I. ORIGIN OF LIFE

Before we make a transition from macromolecules to living cells, we should try to understand how life started in the first place. To understand the origin of life, we have to first understand the history of life on earth and then how simple forms of life that existed for a very long period of time, originated rather than trying to understand how the complex forms of life came to exist. Once we make an educated hypothesis about the origin of simple life forms then we can test if that is a possible way based on the historical evidence we can collect now or by simple experiments conducted under simulated conditions. In the first chapter, we looked at the emergent properties of life and consider alternate hypotheses that can be tested. Many may believe in the idea that a divine or supernatural force created life on earth. This is mainly a religious belief and it does not allow itself to be tested on a scientific basis.

There are two scientific hypotheses that can be tested to learn about the origins of life on earth. First one is whether life came from another planet (extraterrestrial) or not. This hypothesis is referred to as "panspermia" which based on the proposal that meteors from space came with either simple living organisms or complex molecules needed to start life on earth. Even if this is true, then we need to think about how life originated in the planet of such primary source. This leads to the second hypothesis that life originated "spontaneously" on earth or any other planet from simple atoms and molecules combining under high temperature in the presence of water, optimal energy level, limited availability of oxygen, and other conditions of early earth. Let us look into the details of this second and the main hypothesis currently accepted by scientists.

II. EARLY FOSSILS AND HISTORY OF LIFE

This approach of looking at the past to understand a current event is similar to a detective work of understanding how an incident happened. The detective looks at the current evidence of what is left in that place, analyzes the sample he collects and gathers information about the time frame in which the events may have unfolded. The evidence scientists collect to study origin of life are the fossils deposited during geological ages at different places on the earth. Such specimens are systematically analyzed with the help of certain radioisotopes that decay over a long period of time. Based on the current level of such radioisotopes in those specimens compared to the current isotopic distribution in nature, one can conclude the approximate age of the specimen. Using this approach information has been collected about the geological time scale during which some of these bacterial and eukaryotic fossils lived.

Major Time Lines of Life on Earth

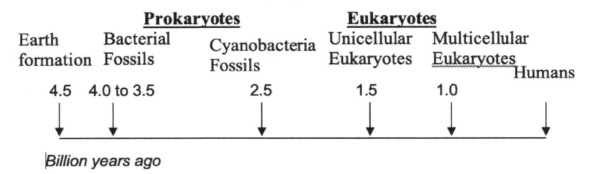

The age of the earth is about 4.5 billion years ago. Life started about 500 million years after the earth formation. Simple bacteria evolved about 3.5 to 4 billion years ago and lived on chemicals (chemoautotrophic). The photosynthetic cyanobacteria (photoautotrophic), originated around 2.5 billion years ago. They were able to fix carbon dioxide into simple sugars and released oxygen into the atmosphere. This made the atmosphere rich in oxygen and allowed the formation and survival of aerobic organisms including eukaryotes. Around 2 billion years ago, the oldest unicellular eukaryotic organisms started to appear and about 1 billion years ago the multicellular organisms appeared. The last 500 million years saw an explosion of various life forms in both plants and animals. The current human genus and species evolved within the last 100, 000 years. Using both fossil evidence and DNA sequence comparisons, we can establish that life evolved from simple to complex forms on earth. Based on both these evidences, we can understand that life started on earth about 4 billion years ago as simple bacteria. The next question is how these simple life forms came to existence.

III. POSSIBLE SOURCES OF LIFE'S ORIGIN

We learnt in chapter 1 that atoms can combine form molecules which may combine to form macromolecules that form parts of cells which in turn can eventually form cells. The transition from non-living chemicals to a living cell may have taken millions or even billions of years and it is not an overnight process.

In 1920s, a Russian scientist Oparin and a British scientist Haldane independently proposed that the reducing conditions (favor adding electrons) in the early earth's atmosphere or near volcanic regions under the ocean may have helped to form complex molecules from simple molecules. The energy to form such complex molecules may have been provided by high temperature and UV radiation. It is virtually impossible to recreate the atmospheric conditions of early earth but you may be able to simulate some aspects of such conditions.

To prove that there is a possibility of life forming from simple chemicals available at that time, based on this hypothesis, Miller and Urey conducted an experiment in 1953 with some basic molecules. They used hydrogen, water, methane and ammonia in a setup with high power electrodes in order to simulate lightning conditions to provide energy for further reactions. After cooling the reaction products, they noticed that simple organic molecules including urea, organic acids, simple sugars, amino acids were formed from this setup. This proved the point that monomers of complex molecules can be formed under the reducing atmosphere present in the early periods of the earth. The next question comes as to where these reactions may take place. Since water is an essential component of living cell, this should have happened in shallow waterbeds exposed to the reducing atmosphere or deep ocean vents that are rich in methane and sulfur. In addition to water and reducing atmosphere, the polymerization from monomers may need a substratum or a solid base to attach. Rock, clay or pyrite (fool's gold made of iron and sulfur) may have been the base for these reactions to occur.

Formation of simple organic molecules is one step closer to forming macromolecules. Once simple monomers and macromolecules are formed, they can aggregate to form simple structures called protobionts. Oparin proposed such ideas and considered these bubble-like structures are essential for cells to evolve and to keep the internal conditions separate from surroundings. These protobionts can incorporate other macromolecules such as nucleic acids and proteins. Simple liposomes (lipid bodies) have been shown to be formed by the aggregation of lipids in an aqueous situation. This is also important to provide some structural support and allow complexity to evolve. The process of forming protobionts from simple chemicals is summarized in the following flow chart.

Atoms → Molecules → Monomers → → Macromolecules → → Protobionts (natural) (reducing conditions) (polymerization on solid support) (self assembly)

This type of accumulation of macromolecules may have happened over millions of years before a right combination survived and replicated. However, such a combination was far from being able to replicate with precision equipped with proper genetic information.

IV.   THE RNA WORLD

For life to originate and perpetuate, you need to have a molecule that can be used to store information and also can catalyze the synthesis of other molecules. Thomas Czech of University of Colorado, Boulder, proved that RNA molecules could catalyze simple reactions. This evidence supported the belief that RNA was probably the first genetic molecule to store information and to catalyze self-replication or even protein synthesis to start life. RNA can help as a template for protein synthesis and for more RNA synthesis. Once proteins (enzymes) are made, they can make carbohydrates and lipids.

It is proposed that DNA evolved later to be a more stable molecule than RNA and proteins evolved to be more efficient enzymes. RNA with catalytic activity is referred to as **ribozyme**. The concept of catalytic RNA provides the possibility of abiotic synthesis of short strands of RNA molecules and their replication. This idea of RNA, being the first genetic molecule, paved the way that all other molecules could have originated along with or after RNA. The evidence of ribosomal RNA and transfer RNA participating in protein synthesis (see the picture of ribosome on right) adds more credence to this hypothesis. In addition, RNA can form variable secondary structures similar to proteins and unlike DNA, which may help in forming ribozymes with different functionalities. This bridges the gap of forming a self-replicating cells or prebiotic structures. RNA is able to do this catalytic work because it can form highly variable secondary structures and it has -OH group in addition to phosphate groups that may help in the catalytic activity.

There are other plausible hypotheses about the origin of life with a metabolic process being the beginning but they need additional support and evidence.

V. CLASSIFICATION OF CURRENT LIFE FORMS

For the first few billion years, the earth was occupied by prokaryotic and unicellular eukaryotic organisms. Only in the last billion years or so the multicellular organisms evolved. The initial classification system, the organisms were grouped into bacteria (Monera), fungi, protists, plants and animals. Recent classification system comprises a 3-domain system, separating bacteria from archaebacteria and eukaryotic organisms.

I. **Bacteria:** Most diverse groups of unicellular bacteria - prokaryotic (prior to nucleus). Bacterial fossils are the oldest fossils known to science.

II.   **Archaea:** Archaebacteria are prokaryotic and they contain some features of eukaryotic cells. Some consider these organisms to be the first life forms that may have formed as they can survive in extreme temperature and reducing conditions.

II.   **Eukarya:** (with true nucleus)
    Eukaryotic Kingdoms:
1. Protista: Unicellular eukaryotes, heterotrophic and photoautotrophic.
2. Fungi: Multicellular and some unicellular, heterotrophic.
3. Plantae: Monocots and dicot plants - photoautotrophic.
4. Animalia: All animals. Multicellular, heterotrophic.

Scientists are currently considering on dividing protists into separate sub- kingdoms as they are well-defined groups within the kingdom Protista.

The timeline of evolution of the various domains and kingdoms is shown on the next page.

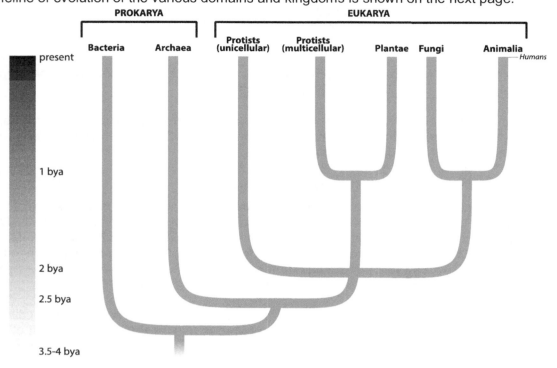

The evolution of complex multicellular organisms from simple unicellular organisms and the evolution of complex internal structures at both cellular and organism level must have been gradual and taken several hundred million years in between different stages.

5. CELL STRUCTURE AND FUNCTION

Concepts
1. Living organisms are made up of cells, cell in unit of life and cells come from preexisting cells only.
2. Cell structure, its components and function can be studied using several techniques.
3. Both the unity and diversity of cells reflect evolutionary history.
4. Information is stored in genes and is expressed in gene products that are used to build cells.
5. Cell structure is dynamic and requires external sources of energy.
6. There are pathways associated with synthesis and delivery of gene products to, within, and outside of the cell.
7. The movement of cells (or organelles within cells) depends on motor proteins and cytoskeleton.
8. Plasma membrane and many membrane structures inside Cell wall and cell junctions.
9. The structure of each component of cell relates to its function.

Outline
I.   Study of cells
II.   Overview of cells
III.   The Nucleus
IV. Ribosomes
V.   Endomembrane system
        Smooth ER, rough ER, Golgi, lysosomes, microbodies
VI. Energy organelles
        Chloroplasts, mitochondria
VII. Cytoskeleton
        Microtubules, microfilaments, intermediate filaments
VIII. Cell surface
        Cell wall, cell junctions

Cells are the basic units of life. As we have seen in the first chapter, there are two major kinds of cells, namely, prokaryotic (without nucleus) and eukaryotic (with nucleus). In this chapter, we will cover the methodology to study cells in general and the details of the structure and functions of all the components of the prokaryotic and eukaryotic cells.

I. STUDY OF THE CELL

The structure is observed mainly by microscopy using light and electron microscope. Function is studied mainly by biochemical and molecular approaches supported by microscopy.

A. Microscopy
There are 2 important factors in microscopy, namely, magnification (how big) and resolution (how clear)
Magnification: The units of linear measurement and examples of what you can observe in such units are as follows:

1 m	= 100 cm or 1000 mm	1 m	human body
1 mm	= 1/1000th of a m	1×10^{-3} m	hair
1 µm	= 1/1000th of a mm	1×10^{-6} m	mitochondria
1 nm	= 1/1000th of a µm	1×10^{-9} m	molecule
1 A	= 1/10th of a nm	1×10^{-10} m	atom

Magnification of a light microscope is up to ~ 1500 x and magnification of an electron microscope can be up to ~ 250, 000 x
Resolution: The resolving power of a microscope sets the practical limits of magnification by any microscope. The resolving power is inversely proportional to wavelengths of light. That is why the light microscope is limited in its magnification power of only up to 1500-fold and the resolution of 0.2 µm. The electron microscope can resolve up to 0.2 nm. The images of the structures viewed under the electron microscope are called ultrastructures.

Light microscope

- Light is focused on the specimen through a condenser lens.
- Light passing through the specimen is refracted through the objective lens and ocular lens to magnify the subject.
- The ocular is mostly 10x magnification and the objectives are 4x, 10x, 40x and 100x magnification.
- It is simple to use and is sufficient up to 0.2 μm resolution.
- You can use the light microscope to observe live specimens in their natural colors or with stains.
- Not much sample processing is needed for viewing under light microscope.

Transmission electron microscope (TEM)

- Electron beams are aimed at a thin section of a specimen stained with metal to absorb electrons and enhance the contrast.
- Electrons transmitted through the specimen are focused and the image is magnified by electromagnetic lenses.
- Used to study internal ultrastructures and cross-sections of cells or structures.

Scanning electron microscope (SEM)

- Electron beams scan the surface of a specimen coated with gold.
- Scanning beams excite the secondary electrons on the sample surface.
- The secondary electrons are collected and focused by the electromagnetic lens.
- Used to view the surface features and the 3-D shape of ultrastructures.
- The magnified image in both TEM and SEM is viewed on a screen and can be recorded on a photographic film.

B. Cell fractionation

Technique involving centrifugation of disrupted cells at various speeds and duration to isolate cellular components based on their density, size and shape. See Figure 7.3 in the book on page 105.

<u>Fractionation involves a few basic steps.</u>

1. Harvest tissues that are fresh or use stored tissue kept frozen at -70°C or in liquid N_2. This is important to preserve the contents such as organelles, DNA, RNA or proteins which might otherwise be degraded.
2. Grind cells with liquid N_2 or in a suitable buffer. The liquid N_2 keeps enzymes that may degrade the cell contents inactive.
3. Homogenize the cells in a suitable buffer. The solution contains salt, a buffer and some preservatives.
4. Centrifuge at various speeds and for various durations to isolate the components.

<u>Centrifuges</u>

- Microfuge is a small centrifuge that can spin up to 14 k rpm and hold small tubes (0.1-2 ml). It is commonly used for molecular biology experiments.
- Clinical centrifuge can hold 5 to 15 ml tubes and centrifuge them at 1-5 K rpm. This is used mostly in clinical labs.
- Floor model or tabletop centrifuge up to 20 - 30 K rpm, large tubes (1 -50 ml). Present in most cell and molecular biology labs.
- Ultracentrifuge - up to 80 K rpm, large tubes (1-50 ml). Most of them are refrigerated and some are equipped with a vacuum pump. This is the most expensive one and it is used only in some labs. Given below is an example of a Tabletop refrigerated centrifuge.

A. **Gel electrophoresis:** This is used to fractionate DNA, RNA or protein molecules based on their size. The negative charges on the DNA or RNA (due to the phosphate groups) make them migrate towards the anode (+) through tiny pores in the gel, made of agarose or polyacrylamide. The molecules migrate depending on their size and electric voltage in the system. Larger molecules move slowly and smaller molecules move fast. If the voltage is increased, the molecules move faster. Agarose gels are used to fractionate DNA or RNA.

The agarose gels are relatively easy to make but the size fractionation is approximate. Polyacrylamide gels are used to fractionate proteins and DNA sequencing reactions.

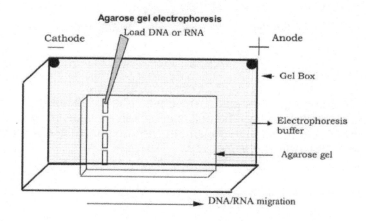

B. **Separation of Carbohydrates and Lipids**

Since carbohydrates and most of the lipids do not have any charges they cannot be separated by gel electrophoresis. Carbohydrates can be initially purified by centrifugation and then various techniques such as calorimetric identification of simple vs complex carbohydrates and spectroscopic analysis will give approximate results. For further identification and determination of their nature, mass spectrometry (MS) and gas chromatography (GC) are used.

Lipids include both polar (phospholipids) and mostly neutral lipids (fats, steroids and carotenoids). Initial separation can be done with Thin Layer Chromatography (TLC) and the detailed analysis is done by High Performance Liquid Chromatography (HPLC), mass spectrometry (MS) and gas chromatography (GC).

Lastly, the sequencing of DNA, RNA and protein can provide further details about an organism and a particular molecular or metabolic process within that organism.

II. OVERVIEW OF CELLS

A. Prokaryotic and eukaryotic cells
There are three domains of life called Bacteria, Archaea and Eukarya. Originally the bacteria and archaea were combined into one kingdom called Monera which is not used anymore. The prokaryotes do not have any nucleus. "Pro" means prior to and "karyon" means shell or nucleus. Prokaryotic cells evolved before the formation of nucleus. "Eu" means truly and "eukaryotic" means truly nucleated cells. Eukaryotes include four kingdoms namely, Protista, Fungi, Plantae and Animalia. All the prokaryotes and most of the protists are unicellular whereas some of the protists and all the fungi, plants and animals are multicellular.

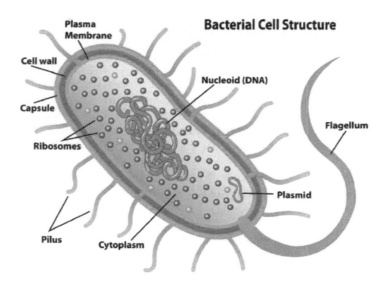

Prokaryotic Cells
Prokaryotic cells such as bacteria and archaea are simple, small, and unicellular organisms with a circular chromosome in a nucleoid region. The cell is enclosed by a cell membrane and cell wall made up of modified polysaccharide. In addition to the single chromosomal DNA there are additional extrachromosomal circular DNA called plasmids.

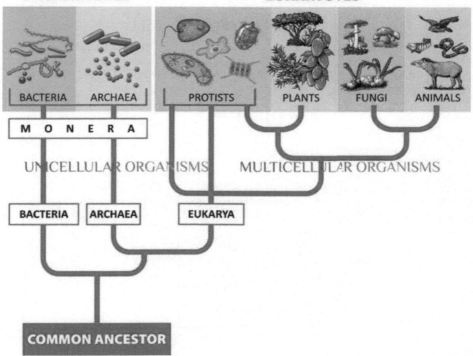

Proka ryotic

- Cells without nucleus
- DNA in the nucleoid region
- No proteins attached to DNA.

- No endomembrane system
- No organelles

- Cell size small, limited by metabolic requirements
(mycoplasma 0.1- 1.0 µm,
most bacteria 1-10 µm)

Eukaryotic

-Cells with true nucleus
-DNA within nucleus
-Proteins such as histones are attached to DNA
-Vast endomembrane system
- Membrane bound organelles such as mitochondria and chloroplasts.
-The cell size is much larger (10-100 µm). Eukaryotic cells are larger about 10 times in diameter,
100-600 times in surface area and about 1000 times in cell volume.

Importance of compartments in eukaryotic cells
Cells are very small in size and large eukaryotic ells are highly compartmentalized for the following reasons.
- It provides, greater surface area/volume ratio
- They serve as partitions between different parts of the cell
- They can maintain unique lipid and protein composition
- Enhance the range of metabolic functions
- Provide localized environments for biochemical reactions
- Sequester reactions such as in respiration and photosynthesis.

Major components of the eukaryotic cell

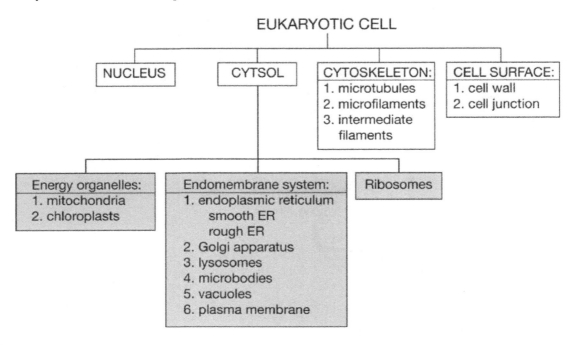

**Fungal Cell
Structures**

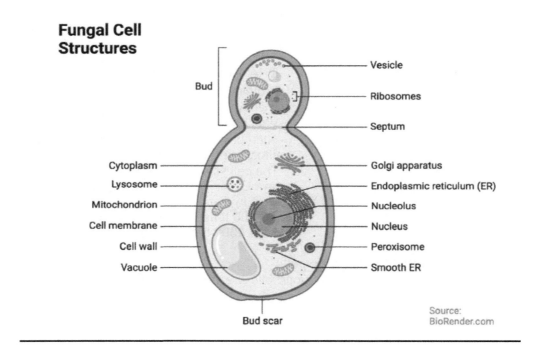

Animal Cell

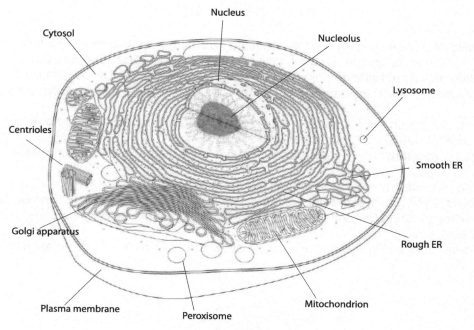

Animal cell

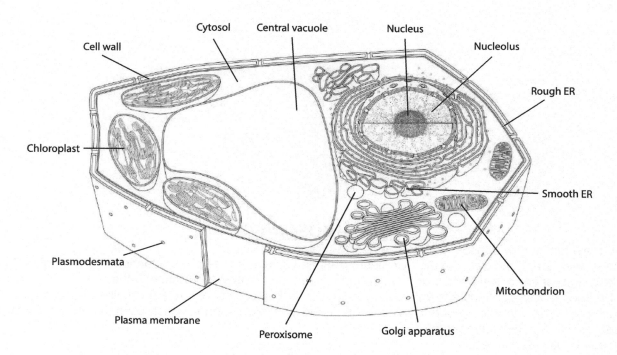

Plant cell

III. NUCLEUS

The average size of a nucleus is 5 μm. It is defined by a **nuclear membrane,** which surrounds the DNA that is loosely dispersed as **chromatin** in an actively growing cell. **Chromosomes** appear only during the cell division. Proteins called **histones** bind DNA. The genes in nuclear DNA contain the program for most of the cellular functions. DNA replication, RNA synthesis (transcription) and RNA processing occur inside the nucleus.

Nucleolus: organizing centers for making ribosomes from ribosomal RNA and ribosomal proteins. The nucleolus contains about 20-30% of cellular RNA.

Nuclear pores on membranes ~ 9 nm - for movement of solutes in and out, for mRNAs to exit and for proteins to enter.

Nuclear lamina: A protein lining inside the nuclear membrane.

Nuclear proteins: DNA polymerase (for DNA replication), RNA polymerases (for transcription - making RNA), DNA binding proteins (regulate transcription), RNA binding/processing proteins, small ribonucleoproteins, etc.

Nucleoplasm: the fluid inside the nucleus is a suspension of DNA, RNA, proteins, fibers, nucleotides, etc.

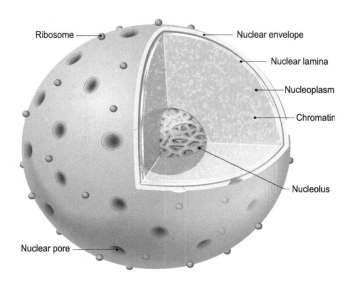

IV. RIBOSOMES

-The main function of ribosomes is to synthesize proteins.

- Ribosomes are found freely in the cytoplasm (to make soluble proteins) or attached to the rough ER (to make membrane proteins). They are also found inside chloroplasts and mitochondria.

- A Prokaryotic cell contains a few thousand, and a eukaryotic cell contains a few million ribosomes.

- Each ribosome is made up of one small subunit and one large subunit which contain different types of ribosomal RNA (rRNA) and proteins.

E.g. eukaryotic ribosomes:

Large subunit (28 S)   45 different proteins + 3 different rRNAs
Small subunit (18 S)   33 different proteins + 1 rRNA

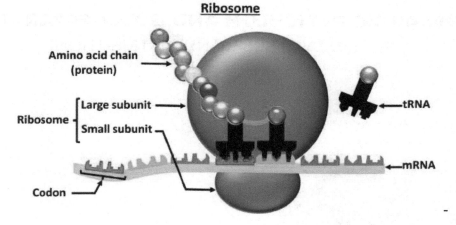

The rRNA is made in nucleus through transcription, the ribosomal proteins are made in cytoplasm through translation and the assembly of each subunit occurs inside nucleolus region.

The ribosomes of bacteria and eukaryotes are significantly different in the size, base sequence of their RNAs and proteins. As a result, antibiotics such as tetracycline and streptomycin inactivate bacterial ribosomes but not those of eukaryotes.

V. ENDOMEMBRANE SYSTEM

The endomembrane system components are interconnected with each other but the lipid and protein composition of the different components may be unique in each of them.

1. Endoplasmic reticulum: (ER) (network of membranes inside the cytoplasm). They are like extended tubules or sacs with internal space called cisternae. There are two kinds: rough and smooth ER.

A. Smooth ER
- Folded layers of single membrane with no ribosomes attached.
- Synthesize lipids, i.e. fats, phospholipids and steroids (including hormones). Smooth ER is abundant in testes and ovaries.
- Participate in carbohydrate metabolism. Catalyze glycogen to glucose reaction.
- Detoxify unwanted chemicals including drugs. The smooth ER content increases in persons addicted to drugs, requiring addicts to take increased dosage to get the same effect.
Cytochrome P-450 and other membrane bound enzymes are involved in drug detoxification.
- Stores Ca^{2+} necessary for muscle contractions. ER pumps Ca^{2+} from cisternae into cytosol to make muscles contract.

B. Rough ER
- Folded layers of membrane. Ribosomes are attached for protein synthesis.
- Synthesis of the membrane bound proteins for secretion and modification.
- Membrane biosynthesis from phospholipids and membrane proteins.

All the protein synthesis by ribosomes starts in cytoplasm. If the proteins contain signal peptide, then a signal recognition particle (SRP) identifies the early-stage protein-ribosome complex and then the protein synthesis continues in rough ER. The signal peptide is cleaved. The proteins made in rough ER are packaged in vesicles (single membrane pouches) before they reach Golgi Apparatus or other structures.

ENDOPLASMIC RETICULUM AND GOLGI APPARATUS
PROTEIN SYNTHESIS AND DISTRIBUTION

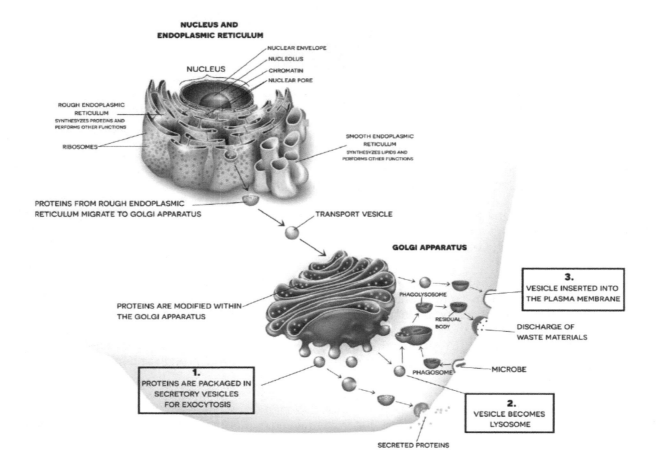

2. Golgi apparatus or Dictyosomes

- Golgi apparatus function like the central receiving and dispatching place where proteins made in ER arrive, are sorted out, packaged into vesicles and shipped to the target sites.
- It appears as flattened membrane sacs with cisternal space.
- It has two sides; cis face for receiving proteins and a trans-face for shipping proteins.
- The modifications on the protein such as addition of oligosaccharides (glycosylation) or lipids (myristylation) occur inside the cisternal space. The Golgi apparatus has enzymes to make oligosaccharides and adds them to proteins.
- The proteins are shipped from the vesicles to other parts of the cell or excreted outside.

3. Lysosomes

- Lysosomes are membrane bags with hydrolytic enzymes that can break down all four kinds of macromolecules. Enzymes come from Golgi or ER.
- The pH inside is acidic, 5.0 compared to 7.4 on the outside, rendering hydrolytic enzymes inactive outside the lysosomes.
- Help digest food and microorganisms (phagocytosis) or organelles (autophagy).
- The digested products are excreted into the cell if wanted or outside if they are not needed.

An example of a genetic disease with defects in the lysosomes is Tay-Sachs disease, which is due to a lipid digesting enzyme missing from lysosomes. The undigested lipids affect the brain.

4. Microbodies:

These are single membrane specialists. There are two kinds:

a. Peroxisomes: Responsible for lipid degradation and detoxification of active oxygen species (O_2^-, OH^-, H_2O_2; highly reactive and mutagenic). Contain enzymes such as peroxidase which catalyzes RH_2 +O_2 ----> $R + H_2O_2$; & catalase which catalyzes

$$2 H_2O_2 ------> 2H_2O + O_2$$

For example, the boy in the movie Lorenzo's Oil had a defective fat metabolism in peroxisomes resulting in neurological damage. It is a genetic disease. That is why a different kind of oil was helpful to alleviate the problem, but it was not a cure.

b. Glyoxysomes: Specialized peroxisomes in plants. Facilitate the breakdown of storage lipids in germinating seeds that store large quantities of oils and lipids. The latter are converted into carbohydrates for the nourishment of growing seedlings.

5. Vacuoles:

Large Central Vacuole: Present in plant cells. The vacuolar membrane is called the tonoplast. The vacuole stores organic compounds, inorganic ions such as K^+, Ca^{2+}, Cl^-, metabolic byproducts, waste products, enzymes, pigments and water. The vacuoles increase in size as the cell ages.

Food Vacuoles: Food is ingested in primitive animals by endocytosis (engulfing into the cell) as food vacuoles, which fuse with lysosomes prior to digestion. Some textbooks refer the food vacuoles as food vesicles.

Contractile Vacuoles: Some fresh water protists such as paramecium have contractile vacuoles that help remove excess water from the cell.

VI.   ENERGY ORGANELLES

Mitochondria and chloroplasts are important for the utilization and generation of carbohydrates, respectively. These are double membrane organelles. They have other functions also. There are several common features and differences between these two organelles. Both are maternally inherited, both make ATP, both are prokaryotic in nature with circular chromosomes and divide like bacteria and both replicate independent of the mitosis in eukaryotic cells. Mitochondrion is found in all eukaryotic cells whereas the chloroplasts are found only in photosynthetic protists and plants.

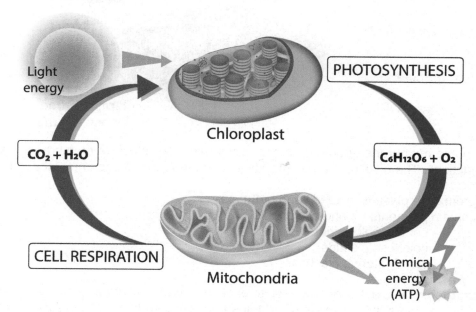

Mitochondrion (singular)
- Double membrane structure
- has its own DNA and proteins
- replicate autonomously

Chloroplast
  - same
- same
- same

- import some proteins from the cytoplasm.	- same
- makes ATP (major source of cellular energy)	- Also makes ATP (mainly for photosynthesis)
- in all higher eukaryotes	- in plants only
- major function is respiration	- major function is photosynthesis. amino acid biosynthesis also occurs.
- DNA used for animal evolutionary studies	- DNA used for plant evolutionary studies

Structure of Mitochondrion

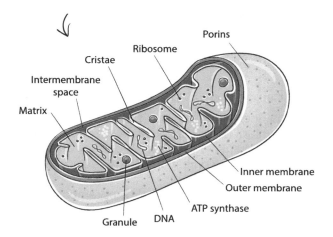

Structure of Chloroplast

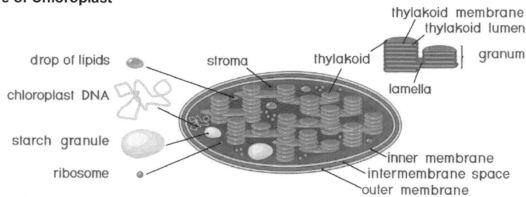

Plastids are double membrane structures in plants with an inner stack of membranes called thylakoid with specific functions. The plastids start as proplastid and then mature into one of the following plastids.

Proplastid   - premature plastids in seeds and embryos
Chloroplast - contain pigments for photosynthesis
Chromoplast   - contain color pigments
Leucoplast   - colorless plastids
Amyloplast   - starch-storing plastids.

Endosymbiotic theory: It is a theory proposed to explain how the eukaryotic cells acquired chloroplasts and mitochondria that have their own DNA, proteins and replicate themselves. Also, their features are more prokaryotic than eukaryotic. According to this theory, early primitive eukaryotes engulfed aerobic bacteria to become mitochondrion (primary endosymbiosis) and some of them engulfed photosynthetic bacteria that became chloroplast (secondary endosymbiosis). Later these organelles developed to become a part of eukaryotic cells and benefitted each other. However, this theory does not explain some other features of eukaryotes such as the nucleus, import of cytoplasmic proteins into chloroplasts and mitochondria, and the process of cell division.

VII. CYTOSKELETON

Three major types of cytoskeleton elements and their functions are shown below.

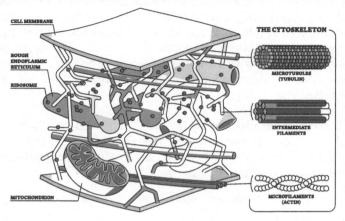

Microtubules	Microfilaments	Intermediate filaments
Structure		
Hollow tubes with walls containing 13 columns of tubulin protein	Solid rods. Two intertwined strands of actin and myosin.	Hollow tubes made up of heterogeneous proteins
Diameter		
25 nm with 15 nm lumen	7 nm	8-10 nm
Monomers		
alpha-tubulin beta-tubulin	- G actin and F actin	- 5 different proteins from the keratin family
Present in		
all eukaryotic cells	actin in all eukaryotic cells, myosin only in animal cells	almost in all eukaryotic cells
Functions		
1. cell motility (cilia, flagella, sperm) 2. cell shape 3. chromosome 4. serve as tracks for movement of organelles	1. cell motility (amoeboid movement using pseudopodia) 2. cell shape & change 3. muscle contraction 4. cytoplasmic streaming in plant cells 5. cleavage furrow	1. structural support 2. tensile strength 3. cell shape 4. anchoring the nucleus and other cell organelles 5. formation of nuclear lamina.

In addition to the cytoskeleton elements, there are some proteins that help in mobility. These proteins attach themselves to microtubules and help in intracellular or cellular movement. Examples of such proteins are:

1.   **Dynein** – attached to one set of microtubules and help in sliding on another set of microtubules. These are involved in ciliate and flagellate movement.
2.   **Kinesin**: This helps in the movement of vesicles on the tracks of microtubules.

VIII. CELL SURFACE

1. Cell wall: Only in bacteria, fungi, some protists and plants. Cell wall composition varies from kingdom to kingdom and also between major classes within a kingdom. Animal cells and Protista do not have cell walls.

Plant cell walls: Contain polysaccharides such as cellulose (40-50%), hemicellulose, cutin, pectin, cell wall proteins etc. Cell wall widths range from 0.1 to several μm. Cell walls protect the cells, give physical support and help in water conservation. Young and annual plant cells contain mainly the primary cell walls, which are thin and flexible. The older cells in herbaceous and woody plants contain primary and secondary cell walls, which are made up of above components and lignin, suberin etc. to make it stronger by adding rigidity to its mechanical structure. Secondary cell walls form within the primary cell walls. The xylem elements in all plants consist of secondary cell wall growth. The layer between the neighboring cells is called middle lamella. It is a thin layer containing the sticky polysaccharide pectin. The layers going from outside the plant cell inwards are middle lamella, primary cell wall and then secondary cell wall followed by plasma membrane.

The cellulose in plant cell walls is degradable by an enzyme called cellulase. This enzyme is made by fungi and some bacteria. Animals do not have this enzyme. Ruminants harbor bacteria that make cellulase in their rumen to digest cellulose. Plant cell walls have pores called **plasmodesmata** which are important for cell to cell transport and viral movement.

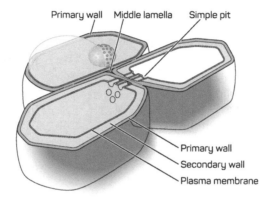

Fungal cell walls: contain chitin which is a □-1,4 linked N-acetyl glucosamine (NAG). The chitin in fungal cell walls can be degraded by a plant enzyme called chitinase (a protective mechanism of plants against fungal infection). Chitin is also present in insects' exoskeletons.

Bacterial cell walls: contain N-acetyl muramic acid and N-acetyl glucosamine (NAM-NAG).

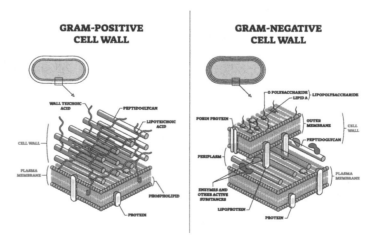

This NAM-NAG linkage can be degraded by lysozyme present in our nasal secretions, tears and saliva (a protective mechanism against bacterial infection). Bacteria could be classified as Gram positive (picks up Gram stain) or Gram negative (does not pick up Gram stain). The differences between the two are illustrated below.

2. Animal Cell junctions. Animal cells do not have cell walls but have an extracellular matrix, made up of glycoproteins and collagen fibers. Some glycoproteins at the cell surface are important for cell-to-cell signal transduction.

Animal cells have three types of cell junctions:

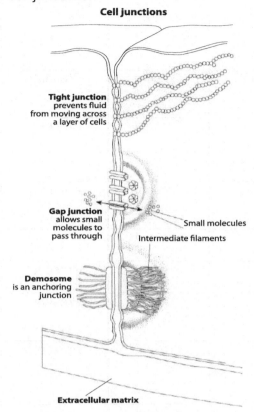

1. <u>Tight junction</u> - two cell membranes are literally fused by integral membrane proteins to prevent movement of any solutes through the space between, e.g. epithelial cells in stomach lining.

2. <u>Gap junctions.</u> Connections between two cells through channels called connexons. These are channels through which chemical signals or solutes can pass from one cell to another. These are important for cell-to-cell communication.

3. <u>Desmosomes:</u> are spots where two cells are connected together by keratin-like fibrous proteins. There are cytoplasmic protein plaques (raised areas) in desmosomes. These are not as tightly sealed as tight junctions. Some space exists between two adjacent cells

This is a very important chapter. It contains lot of details on each part of the cell. Organize the contents into a Table, Figure or concept map and remember the details of the structure and function of each part of the cell. In addition, understand how each structure works in concert with other structures and how the functions of each are related to each other.

Summary of cell parts and their major functions

CELL COMPONENT	PRESENT IN			MAJOR FUNCTION(S)
	Bacteria	Plants	Animals	
1. Cell wall	Present	Present		Protection, shape and structure, and water movement
2. Plasma membrane	Present	Present	Present	Protection, communication, selective permeability, shape and structure

3. Nucleus		Present	Present	Stores chromosomes, DNA replication, Transcription, RNA processing, and ribosome subunit assembly
4. Ribosomes	Present	Present	Present	Protein synthesis
5. Smooth ER		Present	Present	Lipid synthesis, detoxification, glycogen Metabolism, and ca++ storage
6. Rough ER		Present	Present	Lipid synthesis and membrane protein synthesis
7. Chloroplast		Present		Photosynthesis and amino acid synthesis
8. Mitochondria		Present	Present	Respiration
9. Lysosomes			Present	Break down macromolecules and damaged cell parts
10. Peroxisomes		Present	Present	Make and break active oxygen species, Lipid breakdown
11. Glyoxysomes		Present		Breakdown lipids in germinating oil seeds for growing seedlings
12. Central vacuole		Present		Storage of minerals and secondary metabolites
13. Cytoskeleton elements	Present (limited)	Present	Present	Structure, shape, movement and transport
14. Plasmodesmata		Present		Movement between plant cells
15. Desmosomes			Present	Anchoring of two animal cells
16. Tight junctions			Present	Tight sealing between two animal cells

6. BIOLOGICAL MEMBRANES

Concepts

1. The composition of the membrane affects its permeability to specific molecules.
2. Cell membranes function as barriers subdividing eukaryotic cells into compartments with unique chemical environments.
3. Small and medium size molecules pass through biological membrane through active or passive processes.
4. Macromolecules do not readily cross membranes, but there are specialized mechanisms for transport via endocytosis and exocytosis.

Outline
I.   Membrane Composition, Structure and Function
II   Transport of small molecules
     Selective permeability, Diffusion, Active transport
III. Transport of large molecules.
IV. Other functions of membranes
     Metabolic reactions and signal transduction.

Biological membranes are defining boundaries of cells and cell structures. In addition, they help in cellular transport; they are the place of many biochemical reactions; and they participate in cell signaling mechanisms. We will cover the structural features of biological membranes in general and then the transport functions of membranes.

I.   MEMBRANE COMPOSITION, STRUCTURE AND FUNCTION

A. Composition
1. Phospholipids are major components of the membrane. They are amphipathic in nature with hydrophobic tails and hydrophilic heads.
2. Proteins. Integral or intrinsic proteins traverse the membrane and peripheral or extrinsic proteins are bound to proteins on the surface.
3. Other lipids such as cholesterol or carotenoids.
4. Carbohydrates attached to lipids (glycolipids) or proteins
5. (glycoproteins).

B. Structure
The Fluid Mosaic model is the currently accepted model proposed by Singer and Nicolson in 1972, based on freeze fracture studies of membranes. According to this model,

- The membranes are not rigid static structures. They are fluid and an integrated mosaic of several components such as lipids, proteins and carbohydrates.
- The major force binding the membrane is hydrophobic interaction among the fatty acid side chains of phospholipids, other membrane lipids and hydrophobic residues of the membrane proteins.
- Van der Waals forces also operate between the hydrocarbon chains of closely packed lipids.
- Most lipids and some proteins can drift laterally at about 2 µm per second.
- The fluidity depends on the composition of membranes (i.e. saturated vs. unsaturated fatty acids and cholesterol) and temperature. Unsaturation increases membrane fluidity and lowers melting temperature (Tm). Saturation reduces membrane fluidity and increases the Tm.
- The membranes are two sided. The cytoplasmic side is significantly different from the external side. This separation is critical for the functions of enzymes, receptors and transport proteins on the membrane.
- The cytoplasmic side is interconnected with cytoskeleton elements for support and relative positioning of the membrane components.

THE CELL MEMBRANE STRUCTURE

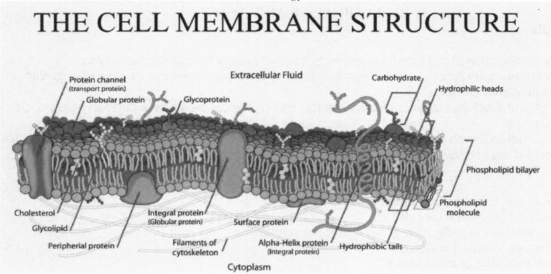

C. Functions
1.   Boundary of cells and its organelles.
2.   Selectively permeable. It facilitates transport.
3.   Many biochemical reactions take place on the membrane or are facilitated by membrane separations.
4.   Membranes are critical for response to environmental changes. They help in signal transduction (receive signals and transmit to other parts in a precise manner)
5.   Important for cell-to-cell communication.
6.   Sequester many reactions and maintain unique local environments within the cell.

II.   TRANSPORT OF SMALL MOLECULES

The movement of small or medium size molecules, both organic and inorganic such as water, oxygen, CO_2, K and Na ions, sucrose and amino acids depends on their size, charge and polarity. With respect to membrane permeability, a small molecule is a relative term and may fit to molecules that are smaller than 100 Daltons. A medium size molecule may be from 100 to 1000 Daltons and anything larger than 1000 Daltons is referred to as large or macromolecules.

A. Selective permeability

•   <u>Through the lipid portion of the bilayer</u>:
- Hydrophobic molecules such as hydrocarbons, non-polar small molecules such as O_2 and CO_2, and polar small molecules such as water can easily pass through the lipid part of the bilayer.
- Medium uncharged polar molecules such as glucose, charged ions (such as Na^+, Cl^-), and molecules (such as nucleotides or amino acids) cannot go through the lipid portion.

•   <u>Through transport proteins</u>:
Specific membrane proteins facilitate the transport of charged ions and molecules across the membranes. They are also called ion channels. There are three types of transport proteins:

   i.   Uniport: Single solute, one direction. e.g. H^+ pump.
   ii. Symport: Two solutes, moving in one direction, e.g. sucrose-H^+ pump.
   iii. Antiport: Two solutes, moving in two opposite directions, e.g. Na^+- K^+ pump.

These transport proteins can be passive or active depending on their energy requirement.
<u>Passive</u>: No energy needed. Transport is from high to low concentration.
<u>Active</u>: Energy needed in the form of ATP, light, or electrons. The transport is against the concentration gradient i.e. from low to high concentration.

B. Passive transport

Diffusion is the tendency of molecules and ions to spread out in the available space until they reach equilibrium due to their thermal motion. The rate of diffusion is affected by the size of the molecule, temperature, electric charge and its concentration. Diffusion is passive, i.e. from high to low concentration without using energy. Diffusion is important for the distribution of ions and other solutes within the cell. It takes a fraction of a millisecond for solutes to diffuse within a cell. There are two types of diffusion to cross the membrane barrier, osmosis and facilitated diffusion.

Facilitated Transport

- Diffusion of charged solutes/ions (such as Na^+, Cl^- or amino acids) through transport proteins (ion channels).
- Passive transport through an integral membrane protein specific for each type of solute.
- Transport is proportional to the solute concentration.
- Analogs of the solute can block transport.
- Binding of solute changes conformation of the transport protein, the solute is transported and the protein reverts to original conformation, e.g. Cystinuria; a genetic disorder with the cysteine transport protein missing. As a result, cysteine accumulates in urine causing kidney pain.

Osmosis is the diffusion of water from high concentration to low concentration through a selectively permeable membrane. Osmosis depends on the concentration of solutes (osmoticum) in an aqueous solution on the two sides separated by a semipermeable membrane. Solute concentration is related to osmotic pressure. If the solute concentration is higher, the osmotic pressure will be greater and the tendency to absorb water will be higher.

- *Hyperosmotic solution* (hypertonic) is one with a greater solute concentration.
- *Hypoosmotic solution* (hypotonic) is one with a lower solute concentration.
- *Isoosmotic solutions* (isotonic) contain the same concentration of solutes. All these terms are relative with reference to another solution.

Water moves from solutions with low solute concentration (i.e. high water concentration) to high solute concentration (low water concentration). The effect of such water movement differs from cell to cell.

External solution	Animal cells	Plant cells
Isotonic - same [solute]	Stable	Flaccid
Hypertonic- high [solute]	Shrivel	Plasmolyzed
Hypotonic Low (solute)	Swell and burst	Turgid

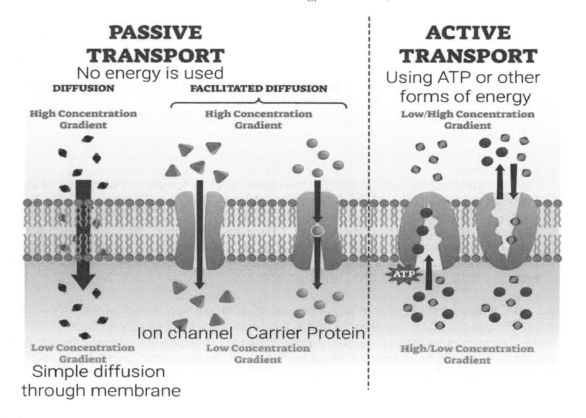

C. Active transport

Energy is used to transport against the concentration gradient. This is the major force to maintain internal concentration of solutes and many biochemical reactions. Up to 40% of the cell's energy is used for this active transport, e.g. Na^+-K^+ pump. An intrinsic membrane protein uses one ATP to transport 3 Na^+ ions out of the cell and brings in 2 K^+ ions against their concentration gradient.

Addition of a $-PO_4-$ group (phosphorylation) changes the conformation of the Na^+-K^+ pump to facilitate the antiport function. After transport, it is dephosphorylated (phosphate removed) to gain back its original conformation.

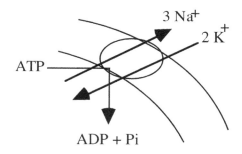

Transport due to electric voltage difference

This is a form of active transport where electrochemical energy is the driving force for the active transport.

Voltage is electric potential energy due to separation of opposite charges.
The membrane potential is the voltage across the membrane ranging from -50 to -200 mV (millivolts). Inside the cell is more negative than it is on its outside. The composition and concentration of charged ions such as Na^+, K^+, Cl^- determine the membrane potential.

ACTION POTENTIAL

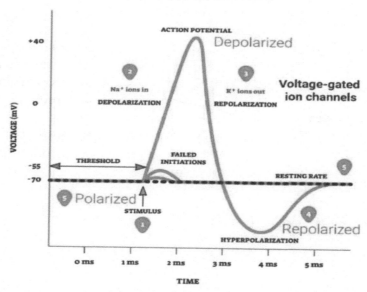

The electrochemical gradient is established from the combination of the membrane potential and the concentration gradient. *Electrogenic pumps* are the ion channels that drive the generation of membrane potential by transporting ions. Ions are transported from one side of the membrane to generate the electrochemical gradient, e.g. H^+ pump and Na^+-K^+ pump. Both make the outside more positive and inside more negative.

Using Redox Potential Energy for Active Transport

Reduction refers to the gain of electrons and oxidation refers to the loss of electrons. The electron transport chain proteins in mitochondrion and chloroplast utilizes this reduction-oxidation (redox) process to actively transport protons to one side of the membrane to generate a proton centration gradient as a form of potential energy that would be used to generate ATP. As you could see from the Figure below, the electron flow from the transport protein complexes T1 to T6 facilitates the protons to be transported from the low concentration in matrix to the high concentration in the intermembrane space. When the protons return from intermembrane space to matrix via the ATP synthase complex, it provides proton motive force to make ATP. This is referred to as chemiosmosis (chemical osmosis). We will see this process in more details in both respiration and photosynthesis chapters.

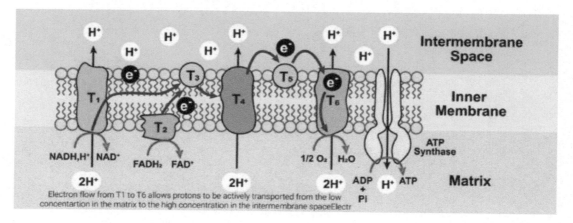

Electron flow from T1 to T6 allows protons to be actively transported from the low concentartion in the matrix to the high concentration in the intermembrane spaceElectr

Coupled transport or Cotransport

When protons are transported by the proton pump utilizing ATP as energy source, this is referred to as primary active transport. When the protons come back into the cell (down the concentration gradient) along with glucose or sucrose, this is referred to as secondary active transport. This is also a form of active transport where the primary active transport system (e.g. H^+ pump) is coupled with another transport system (e.g. H^+-glucose or H^+-amino acid). This secondary active transport is referred to as cotransport or coupled transport.

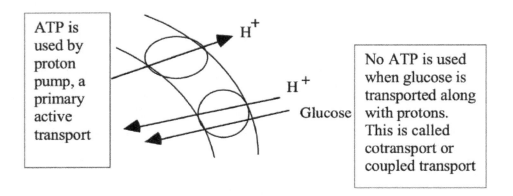

ATP is used by proton pump, a primary active transport

H$^+$

H$^+$

Glucose

No ATP is used when glucose is transported along with protons. This is called cotransport or coupled transport

III. TRANSPORT OF LARGE MOLECULES

Large molecules such as macromolecules (larger than 1000 Daltons), food particles or even whole cells are transported by somewhat different mechanisms.

A. Exocytosis

Vesicles from ER or Golgi bodies carrying macromolecules and other materials to be secreted fuse with the plasma membrane and open outside to secrete the materials.
Examples:

i. Secretory cells – secretion of pancreatic hormones; sweat glands, tear glands secrete bacteriolytic enzymes.
ii. The plant cell wall materials including proteins.
iii. Some viruses replicate inside the cell, package in vesicles and get secreted outside without bursting the host cell.

The diagram below shows how the proteins made in the rough ER are packed in transport vesicles and sorted by Golgi apparatus before packaging again in transport vesicles for secretion.

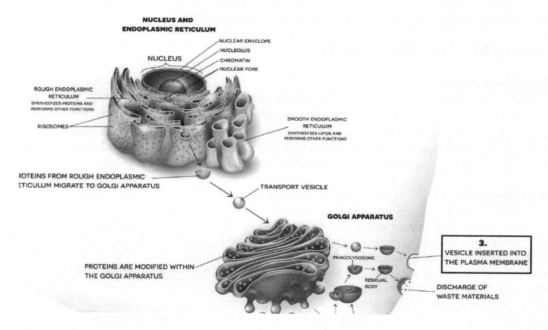

B. Endocytosis

1. <u>Phagocytosis</u>: Macrophages (white blood cells) and amoeba (freshwater protist) engulfing bacteria. Only specialized cells can do this.
2. <u>Pinocytosis</u>: Cells gulping droplets of extracellular fluid.
3. <u>Receptor mediated endocytosis</u>: Specific receptor proteins recognize large molecules such as cholesterol, change conformation and engulf low density lipoproteins containing several cholesterol molecules and related proteins into the cell for processing.

ENDOCYTOSIS

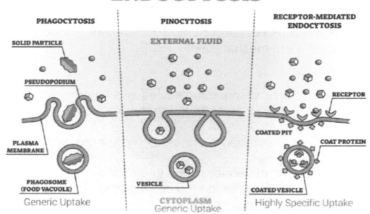

In addition to the above, the transport of the cytosolic proteins into chloroplasts and mitochondria is accomplished by signal sequence located at the amino terminus of the polypeptide. Specific proteins on the membranes recognize the signal sequence allowing them to be transported inside the above organelles. However, the actual process is still not well understood. Also, the transport of proteins from their site of synthesis to their target site is not completely understood.

IV. OTHER FUNCTIONS OF MEMBRANES

A. Biochemical reactions
Several biochemical reactions involved in respiration, photosynthesis, drug detoxification and biosynthesis of membrane proteins and lipids occur on the membrane structures. The energy transformation process needs charge separation (H^+s), as we will see in the respiration and photosynthesis chapters. Charge separations by the lipid portion of the bilayer and biochemical reactions by the integral and peripheral membrane proteins are critical for diverse functions.

B. Cell communication (explained in details in the next chapter)
In addition to performing transport and biochemical reactions, membranes perform the incredible task of sensing external cues and transmitting the signal inside the cell through various mechanisms. The extracellular molecule (the first messenger) binds to a receptor protein on the membrane which recognizes the particular ligand (a specific molecule or the functional group of a molecule); the receptor changes conformation, sends signals inside the cell by a second messenger (e.g. cAMP), which then transmits the message to another inside protein to start a cascade of reactions. Cells can respond to environmental signals by this mechanism. These signals can be communicated all the way up to the genes in the nucleus and make them synthesize new mRNAs to make new proteins in response to the situation.

7. CELL COMUNICATION

Concepts
1. Cells communicate with their environment (including other cells), often by means of cell surface proteins.
2. External signals can elicit changes that permeate the cell.
3. Adjacent cells may communicate directly with each other through cell-cell junction.
4. Signal transduction pathways can lead to gene expression.
5. Almost all cells in an organism contain the same genes, but cells differentiate and specialize as a result of the genes they express.

Outline
I. Overview of Cell Signaling
II. Signal Reception
III. Signal Transduction
IV. Cellular Response

I. OVERVIEW OF CELL SIGNALING
Cell communication is an important process that occurs from the beginning to the end of a cell's life cycle.

Why do cells need to communicate?
The reasons for cell communication can be broadly grouped into the following categories. Some are interrelated.

1. Recognition: Cells need to recognize the neighboring cells as well as other surfaces they contact.
2. Reproduction: Cells and organisms send and receive signals that provide cues for reproduction.
3. Response to stimuli: Individual cells and organisms can respond to different types of environmental stimuli such as light, touch, gravity etc.
4. Growth and development: Growth and development of a multicellular organism require a coordinated effort by the millions or billions of cells that constitute a multicellular organism.
5. Survival and defense mechanisms: There are sensors on the cell surface, which can recognize potential dangers and trigger an appropriate response for the cell to make the defense proteins to protect them.
6. Metabolic functions: Most of the metabolic functions are internal to the cells and are highly coordinated for the cells to be effective and efficient.
7. Movement: It is a form of response at the organismal level due to a stimulus or signal received from the central nervous system.
8. Adaptation to the environment: This is the cumulative result of several signaling pathways in operation over a period of time, maintaining the temperature of internal ion concentrations.

Where does the communication occur?

1. Intracellular communication: The cell communication can occur within the cell itself, i.e. within the cytoplasm or the nucleus or between the cytoplasm and other organelles.
2. Intercellular communication: It occurs between cells located close to or far away from each other. Signals are secreted through gap junctions or communicated by the cell surface proteins on the plasma membrane of the signaling cell to the receptors on another cell located close by (local signaling) or from the endocrine cells to cells located far away (e.g. hormonal signaling).

3. Between organism: It can occur between two unicellular or multicellular organisms. Complex multicellular organisms have various types of signal communication mechanisms depending on their sensory organ systems.

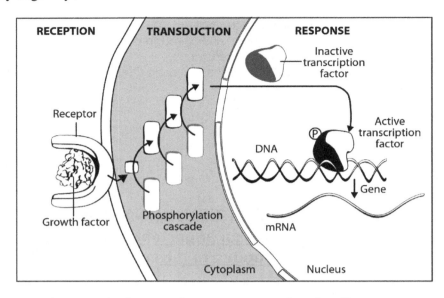

How do cells communicate and what are the components involved?
Signaling molecules such as hormones, proteins, ions and other chemical signals must be present nearby or generated by the cell. Such signals are called first messengers. Some signals are external cues such as light or gravity.

1. **Signal reception:** Once the signal is present, the next step is the recognition of these signals by specific receptors which are integral membrane proteins or enzymes. The signal activates a receptor which in turn activates the signaling pathway inside the cell.
2. **Signal transduction:** Once the signal is received by the receptor, it converts the signal by activating another protein inside the cell which may activate yet another protein and start a cascade of signaling pathways. In this process a chemical such as cAMP (adenosine monophosphate) or inositol phosphate are generated. These compounds are called second messengers.
3. **Cellular response:** Once the signaling pathway is activated this results in the response of the cell or organism in terms of increased gene expression and metabolic activity, growth, defense and movement.
4. In summary, the cell communication can be analyzed in 3 stages, namely, (a) signal reception, (b) signal transduction and (c) cell response.
5.

II.   SIGNAL RECEPTORS

There are four major groups of signal receptors. Among these, the first three are membrane proteins and the 4ᵗʰ group includes soluble proteins. We will see details of G-protein linked receptors.

G-protein Linked Receptors: These receptors recognize the signal and then act through a GTP-binding protein known as G-protein. The G-protein binds to GTP and then activates an enzyme to make an internal second messenger which will cause the cellular response. G-protein linked receptors are similar in their structure but vary in their specificity to different signals. G-protein linked receptors are involved in the embryonic development, vision and taste. Many bacterial diseases such as cholera, botulism and pertussis affect G-protein linked signaling system and about 60% of modern medicines act through G-protein linked signaling pathways.

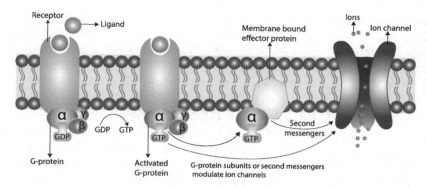

Other membrane protein receptors include Tyrosine Kinase Receptors and intracellular cytosolic receptors which are soluble proteins in the cytoplasm or the nucleus.

Tyrosine kinase receptor

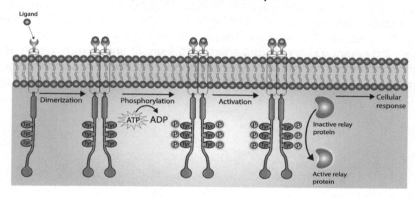

These are specific for a certain type of soluble chemicals that can diffuse through the membrane or lipid soluble hormones that can pass through the membrane easily. These signals will bind to these receptors in the cytoplasm, which are then activated to become DNA-binding proteins. The latter initiates the transcription of specific genes.

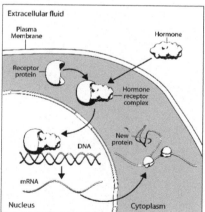

II SIGNAL TRANSDUCTION

Signal transduction refers to the process of translating and communicating the signals recognized by receptors. The signal transduction pathway may involve one or more of the following mechanisms.

A. **Phosphorylation Cascade**.   The binding of the first messenger to the receptor results in the phosphorylation of the receptor itself or the proteins/enzymes associated with the receptors. Phosphorylation is catalyzed by kinases removal of phosphates – dephosphorylation is catalyzed by phosphatases. This is a common mode of activating several enzymes in a phosphorylation cascade for a rapid response to a signal. For example, blood-clotting response triggered by an injury is rapidly activated by phosphorylation cascade.

B. **Second Messenger System.** Second messengers such as cAMP or Ca^{++} are sometimes used to relay the signal inside. The binding of a ligand /signal (first messenger) activates a receptor by changing its conformation or phosphorylating it. Once the receptor is active it activates a G-protein or another protein near by. This in turn activates an enzyme that will make cAMP from ATP or release Ca^{++} inside the cell from endoplasmic reticulum. Such increased Ca^{++} concentration will cause various cellular responses.

III. CELLULAR RESPONSE

The ultimate purpose of cell communication is to elicit a response from the cell at various levels as listed below. The response is sometimes amplified manifold during signal transduction by one protein activating many proteins, which in turn activate more proteins. For example, binding of epinephrine hormone to a G-protein linked receptor will result in a million enzymes that will phosphorylate over 100 million glucose molecules leading to massive amount of ATP synthesis needed during a stress response.

The response may occur at molecular level (DNA expression or protein synthesis and activity), at cellular level (metabolic activity, cytoskeletal organization, cell movement) or at organism level (fight or flight response). Many signal transduction pathways are targeted to specific receptors, which in turn will activate specific proteins adjacent to them. Also, there will be two or more signal transduction pathways operating in the cell, which will regulate the specific response needed for the situation. In summary, cell communication is very important; cells recognize external signals and communicate the signal to internal proteins (causing phosphorylation or other ways resulting in the formation of second messengers), and ultimately causing molecular, cellular or organism responses critical for the survival and reproduction of life.

8. 8. DEFENSE MECHANISMS

Concepts:

- All organisms small or big, unicellular or multicellular must defend themselves to survive and reproduce.
- There are some common mechanisms of defense based on physical barriers (cell wall), chemical defenses (toxic molecules and proteins) and biological components (enzymes and defense proteins).
- It all boils down to the organism with the more efficient molecules and physical traits survive and continue to reproduce and eventually evolve into other organisms.
- The similarity of some of the defense mechanisms highlight the evolutionary relationship that higher organisms have with the ancestral forms of life.

Outline

  I.   Bacterial defense mechanisms
  II.   Defense mechanisms of protists
  III. Fungal defense mechanisms
  IV.   Plant protection and defense
  V.   Animal defense mechanisms and immune system

I. BACTERIAL DEFENSE MECHANISMS

The physical barriers in bacteria include cell wall made up of modified polysaccharides (NAM-NAG: N-acetyl muramic acid and N-acetyl glucosamine) and a capsule made up of slimy layers with polysaccharides that block entry of viruses and antibiotics. The bacteria may also have pili or fimbria with proteins that help in adhering to surfaces. In addition to cell wall, the gram-negative bacteria such as *E. coli* may have an external membrane outside of the cell wall and a periplasmic space. These barriers will block the entry or act as a deterrent for any viral infection or antibiotics entry besides helping them adhere to surfaces and establish massive colonies.

The chemical defense systems include the production of toxins from bacteria such as shigella, tetanus, vibrio cholerae, anthrax and salmonella. These toxins are mostly proteins that will affect the cellular processes of the host cells and lead to the lysis and death or the host cells. Some toxic proteins will form pores in the host cells leading to leakage of cell contents and death.

EcoRI Enzyme Restriction Site

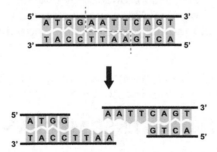

The biological defense of bacteria includes restriction methylation system where the enzyme methylase will add methyl groups to a specific DNA sequence to mark it as their own genetic material and then when a viral DNA enters without any methylation pattern, it will degrade the viral DNA by restriction endonuclease enzymes. For example, the enzyme Eco RI is a restriction enzyme from *E. coli,* that will recognize and hydrolyze DNA sequence 5'GAATTC-3'. These restriction and methylation enzymes are widely used in making recombinant DNA.

Recently they discovered another complex defense mechanism involving CRISPR (Clustered Regularly Interspersed Short Palindromic Repeats) that are left over sequences of bacterial viruses. Cas (CRISPR associated) proteins recognize these sequences and cleave them out.

Antibiotic resistance can be developed by the bacteria by acquiring genes that make enzymes such as beta lactamase to break the lactam ring of antibiotics such as penicillin. In addition, they can block the entry of antibiotic or modify the proteins targeted by the antibiotic through mutation.

II. DEFENSE MECHANISMS OF PROTISTS

The defense mechanisms in protists are not as well studied as the bacterial defense systems. Also, protists are among the most diverse group of organisms that include mostly unicellular organisms and some multicellular organisms. Most of the freshwater protists such as paramecium, euglena and amoeba do not have any cell wall. They are protected mainly by their plasma membrane and they can act as predators of smaller organisms such as bacteria.

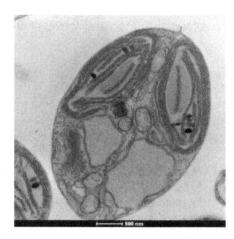

A transmission electron micrograph of a diatom is shown on the left depicting the silica coated cell wall outside and chloroplasts inside

The physical barrier of many unicellular protists such as algae and diatoms with cell wall made up of cellulose, cell wall proteins and other polysaccharides. Some organisms accumulate silica and calcium carbonate in their cell wall. These cell walls are very strong and hard to break. The multicellular protist, Kelp has a leathery and slimy cell was made up of polysaccharide, proteins and minerals, and it is hard to digest or break down.

The protists also make toxic chemicals such as polyketides and non-ribosomal peptides that are toxic to aquatic organisms. Example is the microcystin produced by cyanobacteria and some other algae. These chemicals are neurotoxins and carcinogenic. Algae and diatoms can also produce fatty acid derivatives such as dodecanal to signal other algae and also inhibit the reproduction of herbivores that forage on such algae.

Some of the toxins produced by freshwater amoeba can cause diarrhea and serious sickness in animals and humans. These are very difficult to control or treat with common antibiotics that inhibit only bacteria.

III. FUNGAL DEFENSE MECHANISMS

Fungi has cell wall as the physical barrier and its cell wall is made up of modified polysaccharide chitin (N-acetyl glucosamine). Many fungi undergo an alternate generation of diploid-haploid organisms that can form spores and stay protected until the right conditions arise to survive and reproduce. Fungi produce a diverse group of chemicals that have antibiotic and toxic properties.
In addition, fungal growth is rapid and prolific as you might see the mushrooms that germinate overnight after a rainy day and then disappear to come back again. The largest living organism is an underground fungus that is roughly three miles long in Oregon. Fungal infections in humans is also relatively difficult to control.

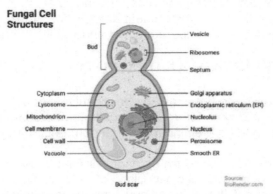

Fungal Cell Structures

Fungi can also make enzymes such as cellulase to degrade the cell wall of plants and kill plant cells resulting in necrosis or fungal rot. Fungal spores can cause severe allergic reactions in humans and breathing difficulty. They can produce keratinase that can break down keratin like proteins on skin and they enter the lower layers of skin and infiltrate with hyphae (roots of fungi). They can grow well at wide range of temperatures including the human body temperature of 37°C.

IV. PLANT DEFENSE MECHANISMS

Plants are multicellular and photosynthetic in nature and they have to literally hold their ground when it comes to defense. They cannot run away but they can defend themselves.

The physical barriers of plants include but not limited to bark, thick layers of secondary cell wall, spines, waxy coating and toxic exudates. Plant cell wall is made up of cellulose, hemicellulose, lignin, tannin and modified cell wall proteins. These chemicals such as lignin and tannin are organic molecules that deter infections by bacteria and fungus.

In addition, plants can make secondary metabolites such as curcumin (turmeric), capsaicin (from chilies) and azardirachtin (neem tree) chemicals which have antibacterial and anti-inflammatory properties. The plant shown below is commonly known as Yellow Bell or Esperanza *(Tecoma stans)* attracts butterflies and honey bees for the nectar and pollen but repels deer from grazing. This variety Golden Star is a popular garden plant in Texas.

Plants also have the ability to regrow parts of the stem or leaves to fight against infection and physical damage to them. Some plants have developed systemic acquired resistance based on prior infection. This is similar to our acquired immunity. Some plants make an enzyme chitinase to degrade the fungal cell wall polysaccharide chitin.

Some plants make toxic chemicals that deter or repel grazing by animals and can emit volatile molecules in the air to warn other plants if there is an imminent danger of animals grazing on them. Lastly, plants have adapted to live in a wide range of temperature, pH and salinity to survive and reproduce.

V. DEFENSE MECHANISMS AND IMMUNE SYSTEMS OF ANIMALS

Animals and humans have evolved to have multiple mechanisms of defense and immunity to infections. The common physical barriers are skin, fur, mucous coatings and some exoskeleton in certain animals. Skin is the largest organ of the body protecting it from random entry of pathogens.

Animals also have the ability to move away from danger or fight to survive. Extreme pH conditions such as the stomach acid or lower pH of vaginal cavity also act as a protective defense mechanism. The tight junctions of epithelial cells prevent the entry of any pathogens unless there is a break in the skin or epithelium. These physical barriers are important for defense but they are not part of immune system.

In general, there are two types of immunity: Innate and acquired or adaptive immunity. The innate immunity is the second line of defense once the pathogens such as bacteria or virus enters the body after passing through a wound in the physical barrier or some bacteria such as Staphylococcus can enter the skin by itself. This innate immunity involves macrophages (white blood cells) that are not specific to any pathogen. The white blood cells can also participate in the acquired or adaptive immunity. Innate immunity includes some antimicrobial proteins called defensins that can kill infectious agents such as bacteria or fungus. The macrophages can release cytokines and chemokines which signal other cells and start a generic immune response such as inflammation, fever and healing process. Mast cells secrete histamines which join with cytokines send signals to dilate blood vessels for faster healing and stimulate the physical response such as sneezing and coughing to get rid of the pathogens.

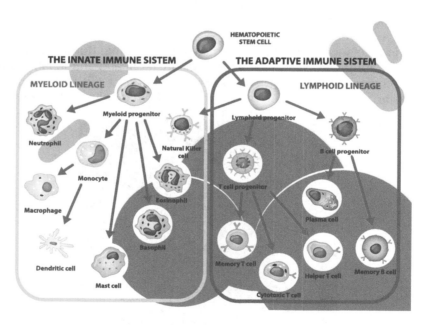

The adaptive immunity forms the third line of defense which is highly specialized. It remembers the nature of the infectious agent and defend vigorously against it when it reoccurs again after developing the. There are two adaptive immunity mechanisms called Humoral immunity (antibody or B-cell mediated) and cellular immunity (T-Cell mediated). In the humoral immunity, the antigen, (antibody generating molecule) a specific protein from a virus or bacteria is recognized by a B-cell and this is mediated by a helper T-cell. The B-cell matures in bone marrow, replicates and activates plasma cells to produce antibodies against that particular pathogen. In addition, the B cell becomes a memory B cell to continue protecting against that pathogen by making specific antibodies. These antibodies can neutralize a toxic protein secreted by a pathogen or mark the pathogen for later degradation by a killer T cell.

In the cell mediated immunity, cytotoxic T-Cell (an immune cell that matures in Thymus a lymphatic organ) directly recognized a host cell that has been infected by a virus or bacteria and kills it by lysing it. This prevents the host cell reproducing the pathogens. The adaptive immunity is triggered when someone is vaccinated for a particular pathogen. The antigens from the pathogen is used for such vaccination.

Overall, there are several common mechanisms across the domains and kingdoms for cellular and organismal defense for the survival of organisms. Such ability to defend pathogens and diseases leads to the survival of the fittest in Darwin's Theory of Natural Selection.

9. INTRODUCTION TO METABOLISM

Concepts
1. Biological systems follow the laws of physics and chemistry.
2. Free energy concepts plain the spontaneity of biochemical and other reactions.
3. Enzymes are the molecular machines operating biological processes.
4. Enzymes are affected by various factors and their activity is regulated by different mechanisms.

Outline
I. Concepts of energy
II. ATP and the cellular work
III. Enzymes and catalysts.

One of the main properties of a living cell, which makes and sustains it, is metabolism. Metabolism means the sum total of all biochemical reactions that take place in an organism. Metabolic reactions produce organic molecules and break down organic molecules. They provide the cellular energy for cells to move, transport and do a variety of actions. The synthetic or constructive biochemical reactions are called anabolic processes and the degradative biochemical reactions are called catabolic processes. Catalysis means a biochemical reaction facilitated by an enzyme for conversion of reactants into products. In this chapter we will study the basic concepts of energy, ATP (adenosine triphosphate), enzymes and their regulation.

I. CONCEPTS OF ENERGY

Energy: capacity to do work. Expressed in kcal/mol or k Joules/mol (1 kcal = 4.18 kJ). There are different forms of mechanical energy.

<u>Kinetic energy</u>: due to motion of molecules or objects. Heat is a form of kinetic energy due to the movement of molecules. Light is a form of kinetic energy in the form of photons moving from one place to another at a particular speed.

<u>Potential energy</u>: due to position, location or arrangement. An object in an elevated place has potential energy. Molecules have potential energy in their bonds. This again is due to the position of electrons spinning in different orbits.

Thermodynamics: The study of heat and its transformation to mechanical energy is called thermodynamics.
- <u>First law of thermodynamics</u>: Energy can be transferred or transformed, but it cannot be created or destroyed, i.e. the total energy of the universe is constant.
- <u>Second law of thermodynamics</u>: Energy transfer or transformation leads to increased disorder or randomness in the universe.

A situation or an object may be a *closed system* (to external surroundings) or *an open system*. All biological organisms are open systems exchanging energy, air, food and other materials with outside surroundings. The universe is considered to be a closed system. The total energy is constant within a closed system but can enter or leave an open system.

Entropy is a measure of randomness (denoted as ΔS, where Δ denotes a change, i.e. condition at the time observed minus initial condition)

Enthalpy is the heat content or the total potential energy (denoted as ΔH)

Free energy (denoted as ΔG) is an expression combining the entropy and enthalpy. It is defined as the portion of a system's energy that is available to perform work when the temperature is uniform throughout the system.

The relationship between free energy, entropy and enthalpy is expressed by the equation

$$\boxed{\Delta G = \Delta H - T\Delta S}$$

T = absolute temperature in K (Kelvin = °C + 273).

If the ΔG is negative, it is considered a spontaneous, downhill or favorable (thermodynamically) reaction and if it is positive, it is considered as a non-spontaneous, uphill or an unfavorable reaction. In terms of free energy release or use, we can group reactions as follows.

Exergonic: net release of free energy (-ΔG)
Endergonic: net absorption of free energy (+ΔG)
   Examples of spontaneous reactions are melting of ice at room temperature and a ball rolling down a slope.
   Examples of non-spontaneous reactions are climbing uphill and refrigerator cooling water.

Spontaneous reactions are favored by:

1. Decrease in enthalpy (-ΔH)
2. Increase in entropy (+ΔS)
3. Decrease in free energy (-ΔG) and
4. Increase in temperature (T)

We can summarize the free energy changes with respiration and photosynthesis as examples:

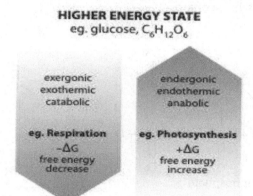

Chemical reaction

The chemical bond energy is the amount of energy consumed to break a chemical bond or the amount of energy released when such a bond is formed. For example, some bond energies are given below.

Bond	C-C	C-H	C-O	C=O	O-H	O=O
Energy(kcal/mol)	83	99	84	174	111	118

Based on the net result of a reaction in terms of heat release or absorption, we can call a reaction:
   Exothermic - heat is released (-ΔH) ,
      e.g. Burning of methane gas.
   Endothermic - heat is absorbed (+ΔH)
      e.g. Dissolving sugar in hot coffee or urea in water.

Chemical equilibrium is the balance between forward and reverse reactions. At equilibrium the concentration of reactants and products remain constant as measured by Keq (*equilibrium constant*). K_{eq} is known as the ratio of the concentration of products over the concentration of reactants at equilibrium. e.g., for the reaction
   A + B (reactants) -------> C + D (products)
   K_{eq} = [C] x [D] / [A] x [B]

The higher K_{eq}, the faster the reaction occurs. For example:
1. Fructose 6-P -----> Glucose 6-P
            Keq = 2.0 and ΔG = -0.4
2. Sucrose + water -----> Fructose + Glucose
            K_{eq} = 140,000 and ΔG = -7.0

From these numbers we can tell that the second reaction is happening much faster, and it is more favorable than the first reaction. Also, one should note that K_{eq} and ΔG are not related but one can expect a reaction with higher K_{eq} to be favorable with a - ΔG.

II. ATP AND CELLULAR WORK

Living cells perform three major kinds of work by using ATP.
1. Mechanical work: e.g., movement of cilia or flagella
2. Active transport: e.g., Na^+-K^+ pump
3. Chemical reactions: some metabolic reactions that need energy, e.g., sucrose biosynthesis.

The structure of ATP is shown below.

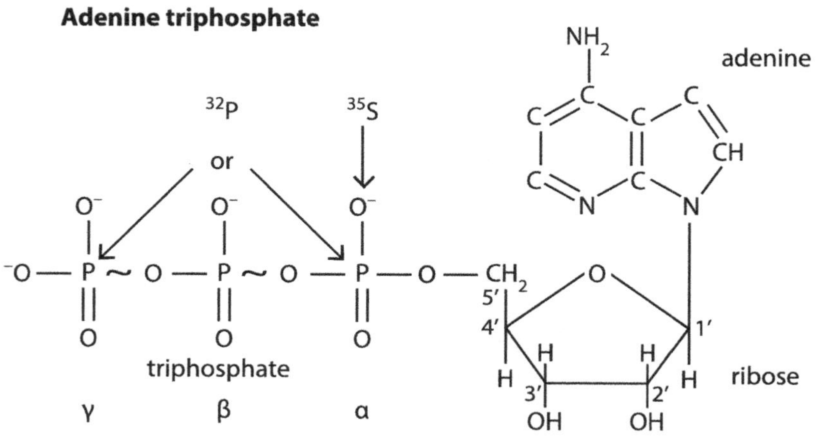

Adenine triphosphate

The bonds (~) between the phosphate groups in ATP are considered high-energy bonds due to the net release of free energy during hydrolysis. They are indeed fragile because of the clustering of negative charges of oxygen attached to the three phosphorus atoms. They have a tendency to hydrolyze in the presence of water even at room temperature.

$$ATP + H_2O \longrightarrow ADP + Pi \text{ (inorganic phosphate)}$$

The ΔG of this reaction is -7.3 kcal/mol (*in vitro*), with a net release of free energy, making it an exergonic or spontaneous reaction. It is much greater (-12 kcal/mol) under *in vivo* conditions.

ATP and energy coupling:
Since ATP hydrolysis is a thermodynamically favorable exergonic reaction, it can be coupled with endergonic reactions that are not spontaneous.

For example, the reaction
Glucose + Fructose ---> Sucrose + H_2O (ΔG = + 6.5 kcal/mol) is not spontaneous because of + ΔG, so an ATP is used to drive this reaction forward.

To make this reaction spontaneous, ATP is used initially to phosphorylate glucose, which is then combined with fructose to make sucrose.

Glucose + ATP → Glucose-P + ADP   (-7.3 kcal/mol)
Glucose-P + Fructose → Sucrose + P_i. (+ 6.5 Kcal/mol)

ΔG for this coupled reaction is − 0.8 kcal/mol

Addition of a -P group ($-OPO_3^-$) to a molecule or protein is called *phosphorylation,* as we have seen before in Na^+-K^+ pump. The enzymes catalyzing phosphorylation reactions are generally called *kinases*.

ATP synthesis occurs in the cytoplasm, mitochondria and chloroplasts, as we will see in detail in the chapters on respiration and photosynthesis. ATP synthesis is an endergonic process as shown below.

$ADP + P_i \longrightarrow ATP$ ($\Delta G = + 7.3$ kcal/mol)

ATP is constantly made and utilized. A cell does not store a stockpile of ATP but maintains a high ATP/ADP ratio. A working muscle cell makes and uses approximately 10 million ATP molecules per second.

III. ENZYMES AND CATALYSIS

A. Activation energy
Enzymes are biological catalysts. Before a reaction occurs, energy must be consumed to break the bonds. This initial priming of energy is called free energy of activation (E_a). This is similar to the ignition starting a car, or using the pilot lamp to light a gas stove. Enzymes do not change the free energy change in a reaction (ΔG), but they accelerate the reaction by lowering the free energy of activation. This is accomplished by some functional groups such as -SH, -OH, -NH$_2$, -COO$^-$ on the side chains of the enzymes.

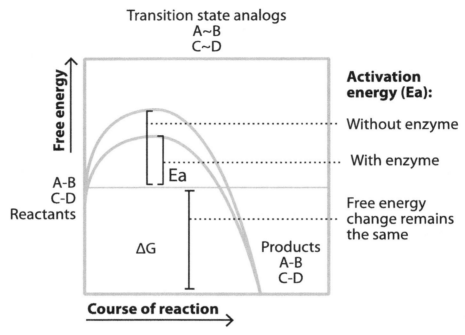

Enzymes have a high specificity for a particular *substrate* (a reactant used by an enzyme), determined by the physical conformation and the amino acid side chains of the *active site* (the site of an interaction between an enzyme and its substrate). The enzyme recognizes the substrate by its molecular shape and functional group(s). The enzyme conformation changes to embrace the substrate and to act on it. This is called **induced fit.**

B. Factors affecting enzyme activity
1. Temperature: Each enzyme has an optimum temperature for maximal activity. The optimum temperature for enzymes in humans is 37 °C, and that for the enzymes in a thermophilic bacteria is 72°C.
2. pH: Similar to temperature, enzymes require an optimum pH condition to operate, e.g., the optimum pH for pepsin in stomach is 2.0 and for trypsin in saliva is 8.0.
3. Salt: In addition to optimum temperature and pH, enzymes require the presence of certain ions or salts at certain concentrations to catalyze reactions, e.g. DNA polymerase needs Mg^{2+} for making DNA polymers.
4. Substrate: An enzyme needs the right kind of substrate(s) to perform the reaction.

V_{max}. is the highest velocity of the enzyme (maximum rate of reaction). V_{max} is achieved when all the enzyme active sites are filled with the substrate (i.e. saturated). The rate of reaction varies with the substrate concentration [S], pH, temperature and ionic strength. It is measured by K_m.

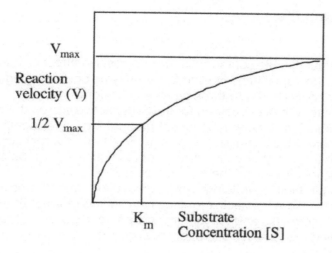

K_m. is the substrate concentration at which the rate of reaction is half its maximum. Each enzyme has a specific V_{max} and K_m. for each substrate K_m. indicates the [S] at which half the enzyme active sites are filled with substrates. Depending upon the substrate, the K_m for an enzyme varies from 10^{-1} to 10^{-7} M.

   5.   Cofactors or prosthetic groups help activate enzymes.

Prosthetic groups can be inorganic or organic and they participate in the reaction by accepting or donating electrons.

a. Inorganic cofactors: Zn, Fe, Cu.

b. Organic cofactors: Coenzyme A, NAD$^+$, FAD, NADP$^+$.

C. How do enzymes work?

Enzymes recognize their substrates by their molecular shape, and functional groups, and change their conformation (induced fit) to fit the substrate and make contacts.

For example, Carboxypeptidase shown above is a protease (a protein degrading enzyme) that can recognize the carboxyl terminus of a protein (substrate), make close bonding with the substrate and perform hydrolysis of the last amino acid at the carboxyl terminus. During hydrolysis, several interactions occur between the active site and the substrate. Contacts between the substrate and the active site of the enzyme may be an ionic interaction, H-bonding, van der Waals interaction and even covalent bonding to make the transition state analog stable and to perform the catalytic function. This interaction at the molecular level makes the reaction spontaneous (-ΔG) and reduces the activation energy (Eₐ).

D. Regulation of the enzyme activity:

1. Activators and Inhibitors

Activators bind to the enzyme, changing its conformation with a positive effect on its activity.
Inhibitors, on the other hand, do the opposite by binding to the enzyme and changing their conformation, resulting in a reduced enzyme activity. There are three types of inhibitors.

A. ***Competitive inhibitors*** compete with the substrate for the same active site on the enzyme. These are usually analogs (similar molecules) with different functional groups, e.g., oxaloacetate is a competitive inhibitor of succinate dehydrogenase which catalyzes succinate $\leftrightarrow$ fumarate reaction. This is reversible. In the case of a competitive inhibitor, a higher concentration of the substrate can be added to overcome the competition. Thus the V_{max} is not altered but the K_m increases.

B. ***Non-competitive inhibitors*** bind to the protein at some place other than the active site, change the conformation of an enzyme and make it less active or inactive. Adding more of the substrate does not overcome the inhibition. So V_{max} decreases and K_m remains the same, e.g., DDT. This is also reversible.

C. ***Uncompetitive Inhibitors:*** Bind to the active site after the substrate binds to the enzyme. This lowers the vMax and decreases the Km.

There are some irreversible inhibitors that bind to the active site and make the enzyme permanently inactive, e.g., penicillin binds to a bacterial cell wall synthesizing enzyme and cyanide binds to a respiratory protein and irreversibly inactivate them. Irreversible inhibition is mostly terminal and it is not employed for regulation.

3. Allosteric regulation:

'Allo' means alternate and 'steric' means conformation or shape. These enzymes have active and inactive forms.

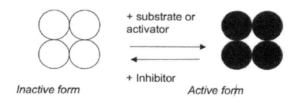

Inactive form   Active form

The following features characterize allosteric enzymes.

a. They are complex enzymes with separate catalytic (binding to substrate) and regulatory (binding to activator or inhibitor) subunits (two or more proteins attached).
b. An activator or inhibitor binds to the enzyme and changes its conformation to an active or an inactive form, respectively.
c. They respond to the substrate concentration in a sigmoid (*s*) fashion.
d. The binding of an activator results in cooperative changes in conformation of the entire enzyme. This is known as cooperativity.

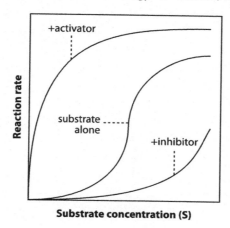

3. Feedback regulation

The end product of a biosynthetic pathway or an intermediate of another but related pathway inhibits an earlier enzyme and stops the whole pathway, e.g., the end products valine, leucine and isoleucine inhibit the first key regulatory enzyme acetolactate synthase in the branched chain amino acid biosynthetic pathway.

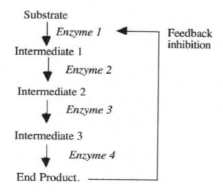

4. Chemical modification

Some of the enzymes or proteins are chemically modified by themselves or by other enzymes to make them active or inactive. The chemical modification may involve adding a functional group such as a phosphate to the regulatory subunit of the enzyme, e.g., phosphorylation by kinases make an enzyme or ion channel protein active or inactive, e.g., Na^+-K^+ pump. Phosphorylation by kinases can add a phosphate to serine, threonine or tyrosine amino acids in a protein. Due to the negative charge of phosphate group, the enzyme conformation changes and it results in either activation or inactivation. There are enzymes called phosphatases that can remove the phosphates.

10. RESPIRATION

Concepts
1. Oxidation of organic compounds drives the process of respiration and fermentation
2. Energy molecule ATP is made in multiple stages including glycolysis, Krebs cycle and oxidative phosphorylation.
3. Electron carriers and organic cofactors such as NAD^+ and FAD are essential to transfer electrons from organic molecules through various processes to make ATP.
4. Oxygen is the ultimate acceptor of electrons driving the oxidation process of organic compounds in respiration.
5. In the absence of oxygen, anaerobic fermentation forms small amounts of ATP and lactate or ethanol as byproducts.

Outline

I. Basic Concepts
II.   Glycolysis
III. Acetyl COA Formation
IV. Krebs Cycle
V. Oxidative Phosphorylation
VI. Anaerobic Fermentation

Respiration is essential for life to generate ATP and various organic compounds from the main energy storage compounds; carbohydrates, fats and proteins. Respiration is defined as an aerobic process wherein oxygen is consumed to break down carbohydrates, fats or proteins to generate ATP and the two major byproducts: water and carbon dioxide. In the absence of oxygen, cells carry out fermentation that utilizes only carbohydrates and generate small amounts of ATP. Respiration occurs in a series of steps as summarized in this chapter.

I. BASIC CONCEPTS
A. Respiration
A basic, simplified and general equation for aerobic respiration is as follows.
glucose + oxygen → carbon dioxide + water + energy
$C_6H_{12}O_6 + 6O_2$ → $6CO_2 + 6 H_2O$ + ~30-32 ATP.

Respiration occurs in 4 major processes in different locations inside cell.
1. Glycolysis - in cytoplasm
2. Acetyl CoA formation - in mitochondria
3. Krebs cycle - mainly in the matrix.
4. Oxidative phosphorylation - on the inner membrane of mitochondria.
Respiration can utilize the energy compounds: carbohydrates, fats and proteins, each entering at different steps to generate ATP.

B. Reduction - Oxidation (redox) reactions

Many reactions that occur in the cell involve reduction and oxidation. Reduction is gain of electrons or loss of oxygen. Oxidation on the other hand is gain of oxygen or loss or electrons. Remember the saying "OIL RIG" which refers to Oxidation is loss and reduction is gain of electrons.

Examples of Reduction and Oxidation

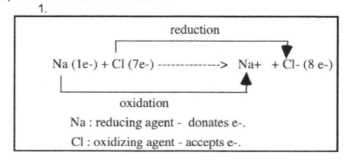

1.

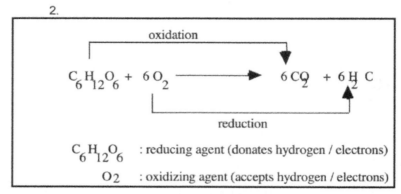

2.

The above reaction 2 represents respiration, which is an oxidation process. The electrons extracted from the food molecules are ultimately lost to oxygen to generate ATP.

C. Electron carriers
Since electrons are very reactive, there are specific electron carriers that help in transporting electrons within the cell.

1. NAD$^+$ - Nicotinamide Adenine Dinucleotide
It has one positive charge and it can carry two electrons and one proton. This is one of the important electron carriers in respiration, transferring the electrons gained in the oxidation of glucose and a few other molecules to the electron transport system to drive ATP synthesis. The NADHs inside mitochondria transfer electrons at a high energy level resulting in approximately 3 ATPs per NADH. There are separate pools of NAD$^+$ (oxidized form) and NADH (reduced form) in the cytoplasm and mitochondria.

$$NAD^+ + 2H \xrightarrow{\text{reduction}} NADH + H^+$$

$$NADH \xrightarrow[\text{oxidation}]{} NAD^+ + 2e^- + H^+$$

NAD$^+$: oxidizing agent - accepts e-.

NADH : reducing agent - donates e-.

2. FAD - Flavo Adenine Dinucleotide
This is another electron carrier in respiration involved in transferring electrons from the citric acid cycle to the electron transport system to drive ATP synthesis. This accepts 2 electrons and two protons. FADH$_2$ operates within mitochondria. It transfers electrons at a lower energy level than NADH, resulting in approximately 2 ATPs made per FADH$_2$.

FAD (oxidized form) + H$_2$ → FADH$_2$ (reduced form)

FADH$_2$ → FAD + 2 e$^-$ + 2 H$^+$

The electron carriers NAD$^+$ and FAD must be regenerated to accept electrons to keep the respiration or fermentation process going.

D. ATP synthesis: ATP is made in two ways during respiration, namely, substrate level phosphorylation and oxidative phosphorylation.

1. **Substrate level phosphorylation.** Synthesis of ATP by transferring a phosphate from a high energy phosphate compound to ADP (adenosine diphosphate) by enzymes generally known as kinases. This process, which occurs during glycolysis in the cytoplasm, generates a limited amount of ATPs. This is the only process to generate ATPs in anaerobic fermentation.
    For example: Phosphoenolpyruvate + ADP → Pyruvate + ATP.

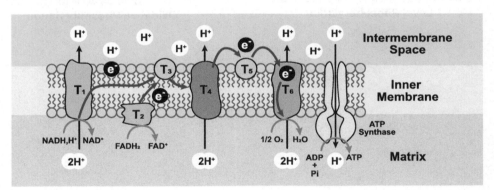

1. **Oxidative phosphorylation**.
    This is the major aerobic process to generate ATPs for cellular energy. This occurs in mitochondria of eukaryotic cells, specifically in the inner membrane and the intermembrane space. In prokaryotes, it occurs on the plasma membrane.

This process is best explained by the chemiosmotic theory proposed by Peter Mitchell. According to this hypothesis, NADH or FADH2 electron carriers transfer the electrons stripped from food molecules. These electrons are then transferred through a series of membrane proteins known as the electron transport chain and are finally accepted by O_2. During this electron transfer process, H⁺s are pumped from the matrix into the intermembrane space of mitochondria generating a [H⁺] gradient. A membrane protein complex ATP-synthase generates ATP by combining ADP with an inorganic phosphate (Pi). When the H⁺s return into matrix through ATP synthase they release the tightly bound ATP. The H⁺s returning to the matrix due to their concentration gradient is called **proton motive force**.

Aerobic respiration occurs in a series of processes as shown in the next pages. Primarily, it starts with glycolysis as most of the energy is derived from carbohydrates and glucose is the most common energy molecule. Other monosaccharides can also be used in this process. This is followed by Acetyl CoA formation from the pyruvate coming out of glycolysis or through beta oxidation of fatty acids. The breakdown of glucose, pyruvate, fats and acetyl CoA releases energy in the form of electrons that are carried by the electron carriers NAD⁺ and FAD which are reduced to NADH and FADH₂. The reduced electron carriers donate the electrons to electron transport chain in oxidative phosphorylation which makes the most of ATP in aerobic respiration. The overall summary is shown in the Figure on next page and the details of each process are explained in this chapter.

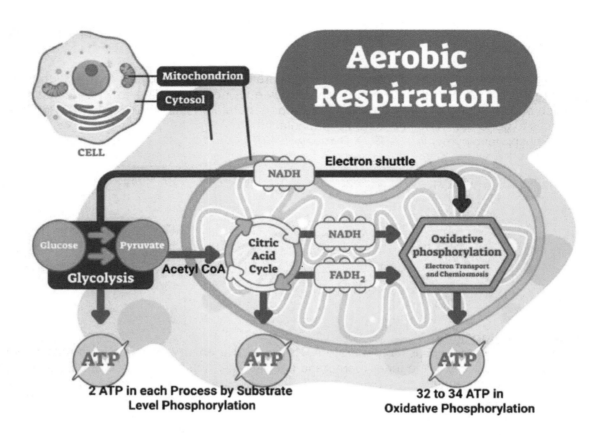

II. GLYCOLYSIS

Glyco (sugar) + lysis (breakdown) - the breakdown of glucose occurs in the cytoplasm through two stages. The first stage (5 steps) is an energy investment phase during which glucose is broken down into two trioses. The second stage (5 steps) is an energy yielding phase.

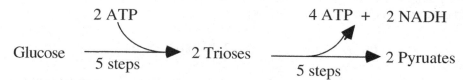

The above is a summary reaction of Glycolysis.

Step 1. Glucose is phosphorylated by <u>hexokinase</u> (hexose- a 6 -C sugar, kinase - phosphorylating enzyme). Mg^{2+} is needed in this first priming event (energy investing) using the first ATP. This is also the first committed step for glycolysis. First committed step means once started, it goes through the whole process.

        Glucose + ATP → Glucose 6-phosphate + ADP

Once the glucose is phosphorylated, (and negatively charged), it is reactive and it does not leave the cell. If the cell is in need of ATP, it is used for glycolysis. Excess accumulation of glucose 6-phosphate can inhibit the hexokinase from phosphorylating more glucose molecules.

Step 2. Glucose 6-phosphate is converted to fructose 6-phosphate. This step is an aldose → ketose conversion by <u>phosphoglucoisomerase</u> to prepare for another phosphorylation.

        Glucose 6-phosphate → Fructose 6-phosphate

Step 3. Phosphorylation of fructose 6-phosphate by <u>Phosphofructokinase</u> (PFK; a kinase which phosphorylates a phospho-fructose). This enzyme also needs Mg^{2+}.

This is the key regulatory step and an important step to remember.

Fructose 6-phosphate + ATP → Fructose 1,6-bisphosphate + ADP

This is the second energy-investing step. This is **the key regulatory step** and Phosphofructokinase **(PFK)** is the key regulatory enzyme that means it can make the glycolysis go faster, slower or stop. This is a complex allosteric enzyme. It is induced by high levels of ADP or AMP (means the cell needs ATP) and inhibited by high levels of ATP (means the cell has enough ATP) and citrate (the first committed product of Krebs cycle- another indication of cells having enough ATP).

Step 4. Fructose 1,6-bisphosphate is split into two trioses by <u>aldolase</u>. The fructose ring opens and aldolase splits fructose 1,6-bisphosphate in the middle into two trioses.

Fructose 1,6-bisphosphate ←>Dihydroxyacetone phosphate + Glyceraldehyde 3-phosphate

Step 5. Reversible conversion of two trioses by triosephosphate isomerase.

Dihydroxyacetone phosphate ←→ Glyceraldehyde 3-phosphate

Dihydroxyacetone phosphate and glyceraldehyde 3-phosphate are structural isomers. The equilibrium is towards glyceraldehyde 3-phosphate because it is utilized by the next 5 steps of glycolysis rapidly.

In the above set of 5 reactions, 2 ATPs have been invested per glucose.

The following 5 reactions will yield 4 ATPs per glucose. Since each of the trioses in step 5 will undergo these reactions there will be two such reactions from step 6 through step 10, for each glucose.

Step 6. Oxidation of Glyceraldehyde 3- Phosphate (G3P) and phosphorylation to generate 1,3-bisphosphoglycerate (BPG) by <u>triose phosphate dehydrogenase</u>.

One proton (H^+) and two electrons are removed (oxidation) from G3P and another low energy phosphate (inorganic phosphate) is added at the 1st C to generate 1,3 BPG. The electrons and proton are transferred to NAD^+ (oxidizing agent), which gets reduced to NADH. NADH transfers electrons to the electron transport chain to generate ATP inside mitochondria.

$$Pi \; + \; 2\;NAD^+ \qquad 2\;NADH \; + \; H^+$$

2 (Glyceraldehyde3-Phosphate) ⟶ 2 (1,3-Bisphosphoglycerate)

Triose phosphate dehydrogenase

The enzyme triose phosphate dehydrogenase is a complex enzyme which can perform both oxidation and phosphorylation simultaneously. The presence of a -SH group in its active sites helps to perform these reactions.

Arsenate poisoning: *The poison arsenate (AsO_4^{3-}) uncouples the phosphorylation and oxidation by competing with PO_4^{2-} for this -SH site. The resulting arseno-3 phosphoglycerate is not stable and no ATP is made from this reaction. Similar inhibitions with other phosphorylation reactions result from arsenic poisoning.*

Step 7. First ATP synthesis by transferring high energy phosphate group from 1,3 BPG to ADP (substrate level phosphorylation). This is the first yield of 2 ATPs from two trioses balancing the first investment of 2 ATPs per glucose.

$$2\;ADP \qquad\qquad 2\;ATP$$

2 (1, 3- Bisphosphoglycerate) ⟶ 2 (3- phosphoglycerate)

Step 8. Transfer of phosphate from 3rd to 2nd C. The phosphate group of 3-phosphoglycerate is transferred from 3rd C to 2nd C to generate 2-phosphoglycerate by <u>phosphoglyceromutase</u>.

2 (3-phosphoglycerate) ⟶ 2 (2-phosphoglycerate)

Phosphoglyceromutase

Step 9. Removal of H_2O from 2-PGA. A water molecule is removed from 2-PGA by enolase to create a double bond between the 2nd C and 3rd C to generate the 2-P bond unstable in the new compound phosphoenolpyruvate (PEP).

$$2\;H_2O$$

2 (2-phosphoglycerate) ⟶ 2 (Phosphoenolpyruvate)

Step 10. Second ATP synthesis. The phosphate from PEP is transferred to ADP (second substrate level phosphorylation) to generate two more ATPs which is the net ATP synthesis in cytoplasm during glycolysis.

$$2\;ADP \qquad\qquad 2ATP$$

2 Phosphoenolpyruvate ⟶ 2 Pyruvate

Glycolysis

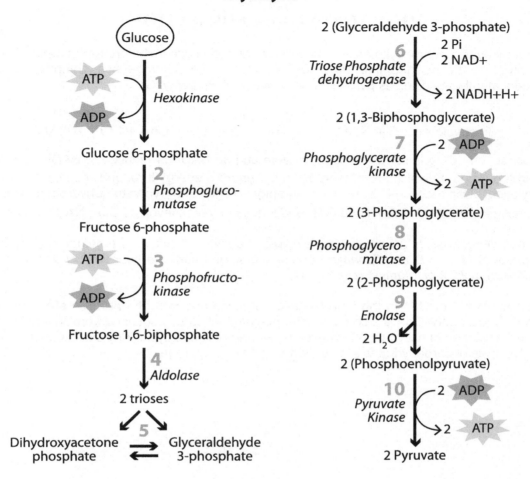

Remember only the net inputs, outputs and the details of only the key steps 1 and 3 in this entire pathway and not each step. Do not worry about remembering any of the chemical structures and all the steps in the pathway.

Summary of reactions in glycolysis *(Remember the net inputs and outputs)*

(Inputs) Glucose + 2 NAD$^+$ + 2 ADP + 2 P$_i$ → (Outputs) 2 Pyruvate + 2 NADH + 2 H$^+$ + 2 ATP

Electron Shuttles

The 2 pyruvates are transferred into mitochondria by a specific transport protein. The 2 ATPs made are used in cytoplasm. In aerobic respiration, the NADH transfers its electrons to a mitochondrial- FAD or NAD$^+$ to be used in electron transport chain. Since NADH is a large molecule, it cannot enter the mitochondria and this e$^-$ transfer into mitochondria is done by a shuttle mechanism. Two such mechanisms are glycerol 3- phosphate shuttle and malate-aspartate shuttle. The NAD$^+$ should be regenerated to keep the glycolysis going. The shuttle helps in the regeneration of NAD$^+$ needed in glycolysis.

1. Glycerol 3-phosphate shuttle. The NADH from glycolysis transfers the electrons to dihydroxy acetone phosphate (DHAP) to form glycerol 3-phosphate, which diffuses into mitochondria wherein the electrons are transferred to mitochondrial FAD to generate FADH$_2$ and dihydroxy acetone phosphate. The dihydroxy acetone phosphate diffuses out to perform the shuttle reaction again. The NAD$^+$ regenerated in cytoplasm returns to glycolysis to accept another pair of electrons.

2. Malate-Aspartate. In heart and liver cells the cytoplasmic NADH transfers electrons to a mitochondrial NADH by a different shuttle namely malate-aspartate shuttle. In this case, the mitochondrial NADH results in making 3 ATPs for each NADH from glycolysis. The FADH$_2$ made in the first shuttle mechanism results in only 2 ATPs for each NADH from glycolysis.

III.   ACETYL CoA FORMATION

This step of pyruvate decarboxylation and acetyl CoA formation occurs before Krebs cycle. The pyruvate from glycolysis is transported into mitochondria. Pyruvate dehydrogenase complex on the inner mitochondrial membrane oxidizes pyruvate and converts it into acetyl CoA.

$$\text{Pyruvate} + \text{CoA} + \text{NAD}^+ \longrightarrow \text{Acetyl CoA} + CO_2 + \text{NADH}$$

In this process, one CO_2 is released from pyruvate and an NAD^+ is reduced to NADH. Acetyl CoA is also generated from fats which are broken down to generate energy through Krebs cycle and oxidative phosphorylation. This reaction is irreversible and highly regulated. Pyruvate dehydrogenase is inhibited by high levels of acetyl CoA, NADH and GTP and induced by high levels of CoA, NAD^+, GDP.

Pyruvate dehydrogenase is a complex protein with 3 enzymes combined together and uses thiamine pyrophosphate (TPP), FAD and lipoamide as cofactors. Beri beri is a neurological and cardiovascular disorder caused by lack of thiamine (vitamin B1).

Acetyl CoA is also formed from the beta-oxidation of lipids and from the proteins after hydrolysis and deamination. Thus, acetyl CoA is a common intermediate that can be obtained from carbohydrates, lipids and proteins. This step of acetyl CoA formation is not part of Krebs cycle. Any excess acetyl CoA formed from the glycolysis of carbohydrates are converted to fats for storage.

IV.   KREBS CYCLE

The Krebs cycle was named after Hans Krebs who elucidated most of the pathway. This is also called the Tricarboxylic Acid (TCA) Cycle or Citric Acid Cycle. This process occurs mainly in the matrix and on the inner membrane of mitochondria.

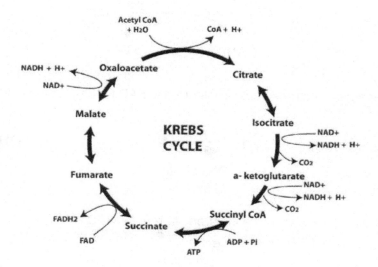

Step 1. This is the first committed step performed by <u>citrate synthase </u>which is induced by AMP and inhibited by ATP.

$$Acetyl\ CoA\ (2\ C) + Oxaloacetate\ (4\ C) \xrightarrow{H_2O} Citrate\ (6\ C)\ +\ CoA + H^+$$

Step 2. This isomerization is done through dehydration and hydration of citrate through an intermediate

$$Citrate\ (6\text{-}C) \underset{aconitase}{\overset{}{\rightleftarrows}} Isocitrate\ (6\text{-}C)$$

cis-aconitate by aconitase.

Step 3.   Oxidative decarboxylation of isocitrate by <u>isocitrate dehydrogenase</u>. This is the rate limiting step (controls the reaction rate of Krebs cycle). Isocitrate dehydrogenase is stimulated by ADP which enhances its affinity for its substrates isocitrate and NAD^+. The enzyme is inhibited by high levels of NADH and ATP.

$$Isocitrate\ (6\text{-}C) \xrightarrow{NAD^+ + H^+ \quad\to\quad NADH\ +\ CO_2\ +\ H^+} a\text{-}ketoglutarate\ (5\text{-}C)$$

Step 4. This is the third level of control in the Krebs cycle. NADH, succinyl CoA and ATP inhibits the activity of a-ketoglutarate dehydrogenase. So far 2 CO_2 molecules have been released from Krebs cycle from the 6-C compound citrate resulting in the 4-C compound succinate which will be gradually converted into oxaloacetate in the following steps (5 to 8) to continue the cycle.

$$a\text{-}ketoglutarate\ +\ CoA \xrightarrow[a\text{-}ketoglutarate\ dehydrogenase]{NAD^+ \quad\quad NADH\ +\ CO_2} Succinyl\ CoA\ (4\text{-}C)$$

Step 5. This reaction results in the substrate level phosphorylation of ADP to generate an ATP by transferring the phosphate from GTP to ADP. The Pi (pyrophosphate) is obtained from the matrix.

$$\text{Succinyl CoA} + Pi + GDP \rightleftharpoons \text{Succinate} + GTP + CoA$$

Succinyl CoA synthetase

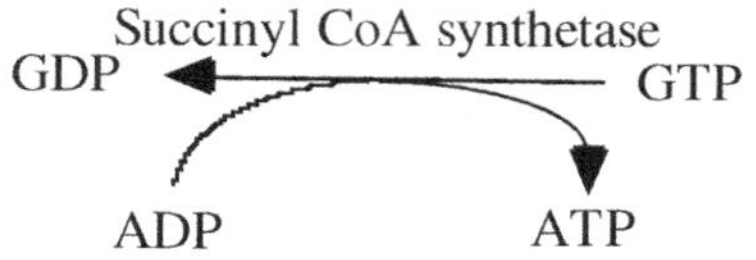

GDP ← → GTP

ADP   ATP

Step 6. This is another set of electrons being transferred to FAD for later use in oxidative phosphorylation.

$$\text{Succinate} + FAD \rightleftharpoons \text{Fumarate} + FADH_2$$

Succinate
dehydragenase

Step 7. This a preparation to extract more electrons to reduce NAD^+

$$\text{Fumarate} + \tfrac{1}{2} \rightleftharpoons \text{Malate}$$

Fumarase

Step 8. This is the last NADH made in Krebs cycle. So far 2 NADH, 1 ATP and 1 $FADH_2$ have been made from each acetyl CoA that enters Krebs cycle.

$$\text{Malate} + NAD^+ \rightleftharpoons \text{Oxaloacetate} + NADH$$

Malate dehydrogenase

Summary of Krebs cycle reactions *(Remember this)*

(Inputs) Acetyl CoA + 3 NAD^+ + FAD + ADP + Pi + 2H_2O $\rightarrow$

(Outputs)   2 CO_2 + 3 NADH + 3H^+ + $FADH_2$ + ATP + CoA

V. OXIDATIVE PHOSPHORYLATION

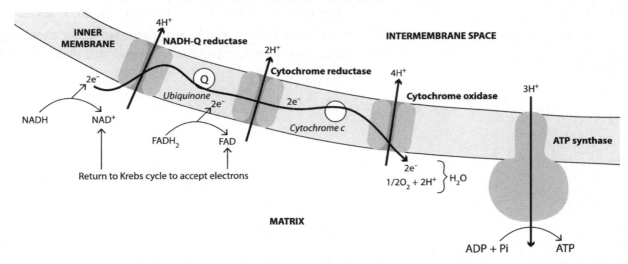

Oxidation in this case refers to the loss of electrons from NADH and $FADH_2$ to a series of membrane proteins, which finally transfer them to oxygen, the final electron acceptor, to generate water (along with $2 H^+$).

During this process of electron transfer, protons are pumped out of the matrix into the intermembrane space making it acidic (proton gradient). As the protons (proton motive force) return to the matrix through ATP synthase they help in the formation and release of ATP from the enzyme. This whole process is referred to as oxidative phosphorylation.

Transfer of electrons from NADH and $FADH_2$ to electron transport chain:

NADH transfers the electrons to NADH-Q reductase and gets reduced to NAD^+ which returns to the mitochondrial NAD^+ pool to accept electrons from the Krebs cycle. $FADH_2$ transfers electrons at a lower energy level to ubiquinone (Coenzyme Q-10 or CoQ10), a mobile electron carrier. $FADH_2$ then becomes FAD and returns to Krebs cycle. Krebs cycle cannot continue without having enough NAD^+ and FAD for the oxidation of acetyl CoA. Since $FADH_2$ delivers electrons at the lower energy level, fewer ATPs are made from its electron transfer as explained in next paragraph.

The electrons from NADH and $FADH_2$ are transferred through cytochrome reductase and cytochrome oxidase and finally are accepted by oxygen (the molecular oxygen is used here). Oxygen is the ultimate electron acceptor in aerobic respiration. The two electrons, two protons (from matrix) and oxygen from O_2 generates water in matrix. Note that the CO_2 had been released from decarboxylation of pyruvate and from Krebs cycle long before O_2 is consumed in oxidative phosphorylation.

Generation of $[H^+]$ gradient and ATP synthesis:
When the electrons are transferred through the membrane proteins, they generate an electrical imbalance resulting in transfer of protons from matrix into intermembrane space. The specific details are not well known. For each pair of electrons, approximately 2 to 4 protons are transported into the intermembrane space. When approximately 3 protons return from the intermembrane space into matrix through the ATP synthase this proton motive force helps to release ATP which is made by and tightly bound to the enzyme. Another proton is used to transport the ATP from the matrix to cytoplasm through a membrane protein **ATP/ADP-translocase**. So approximately 3-4 protons are needed to make and transport 1 ATP. Since NADH and $FADH_2$ results in the transport of approximately 10 and 6 protons respectively, they result in making 3 and 2 ATPs each respectively.

Respiratory poisons
The three classes of respiratory poisons, their mechanism of action and the examples are as follows.
1. <u>Uncouplers of proton gradient</u>: Abolish proton gradient by making the membrane leaky, resulting in no ATP synthesis. E.g. dinitrophenol (DNP).

2. <u>ATP synthase inhibitors</u>: directly binds to ATP synthase and inhibits ATP synthesis. E.g. oligomycin.

3. <u>Electron transport inhibitors</u>: Blocks the electron transport at various stages. These result in reduced or lack of proton gradient and ATP synthesis but their main effect is in blocking O_2 from accepting electrons stopping the regeneration of NAD^+ and FAD without which Krebs cycle cannot function. E.g. Cyanide (CN^-), carbon monoxide (CO) and azide (N^{3-}) all bind to cytochrome oxidase and block electron transfer to O_2.

VI. ANAEROBIC RESPIRATION AND FERMENTATION

A. Anaerobic respiration (Complete respiration without oxygen). In this process, either NO_3^- or SO_4^- accepts the electrons from electron transport chain instead of O_2. All the other reactions go on in a similar manner. This process is limited to facultative anaerobes that can live under a NO_3^- or SO_4^- rich environment.

B. Anaerobic fermentation

No oxygen or any other molecule is available to receive electrons from the electron transport chain. ATPs are made through glycolysis only. NAD^+ needs to be regenerated to keep the glycolysis going. This is achieved either through alcoholic fermentation or lactic acid fermentation as explained below.

1. Alcohol Fermentation

The two pyruvates made from glucose during glycolysis are decarboxylated by pyruvate decarboxylase to generate acetaldehyde. The CO_2 released during this decarboxylation is what makes bread rise and beer froth. The acetaldehyde is hydrogenated to form ethanol, using NADH as the reducing agent by alcohol dehydrogenase thus regenerating the NAD+ needed for the glycolysis to continue. Alcohol is a byproduct in alcoholic fermentation.

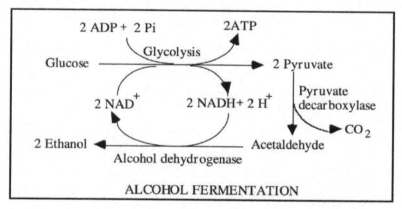

ALCOHOL FERMENTATION

2. Lactic acid fermentation

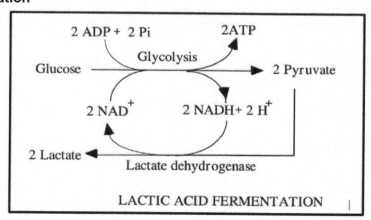

LACTIC ACID FERMENTATION

Pasteur Effect

Louis Pasteur observed that the yeast growing under anaerobic conditions consumed more sugar than the yeast grown under aerobic conditions. This is called the Pasteur effect and it can be explained by the fact that yeast generates less ATP (2/glucose) under anaerobic conditions than under aerobic conditions (30 - 32 ATPs/glucose). So, to maintain same growth rate, anaerobic yeast consumes a lot more sugar, actually up to 100 times more than aerobic yeast does.

Animals do not have pyruvate decarboxylase and so they perform lactic acid fermentation in the muscle cells to regenerate NAD+ during O_2 deprivation.

In muscle cells, NAD^+ is regenerated by converting the pyruvate into lactate which returns to liver to be reconverted to glucose for later use. The lactic acid accumulation and micro tears causes muscle fatigue during strenuous exercise with limited O_2 levels. Lactate fermentation is an important contributor for quick burst of energy under emergency situations.

Concepts

1. The ultimate source of energy for almost all living systems is the sun.
2. Series of reactions occur in photosynthetic cells to harvest light energy in the form of ATP and NADPH.
3. Plants and other photosynthetic organisms have special structures and molecules to harness the sun's energy.
4. The chemical energy in the form of ATP and NADPH are used to fix CO2 in the form of carbohydrates for energy, storage and making other organic molecules.

Outline

I. Basic concepts
   Leaf anatomy, basic reactions, light energy and pigments.
II. Light dependent reactions
   Photosystem I and II, cyclic and non-cyclic Photophosphorylation

III. Calvin Cycle:

IV. Carbon fixation, photorespiration

IV. Variations of Calvin cycle
   C3, C4 and CAM pathways

The ultimate source of energy for this living planet comes from the sun. Photosynthetic algae, bacteria and plants can utilize the solar energy to fix atmospheric CO_2 into carbohydrates. Photosynthesis generates carbohydrates and other organic compounds from which all other organic molecules are made. This chapter covers the structure of the photosynthetic apparatus; how light energy is transformed into chemical energy; how CO_2 is fixed into organic molecules and some of the variations within photosynthesis. We will focus mainly on photosynthesis in plants.

I.   BASIC CONCEPTS

Based on how an organism obtains its food, we can classify them into the following categories.

Autotrophic organisms make their own food by biochemical processes. They generate carbon compounds and their own food from chemicals from surroundings (chemoautotrophic, e.g. bacteria) or through photosynthesis (photoautotrophic, e.g. plants, photosynthetic bacteria, and algae).

Heterotrophic organisms survive by feeding on other organisms. Animals, fungi and many bacteria are heterotrophs. They depend on photoautotrophs for food and also oxygen that is released during photosynthesis.

A. Leaf anatomy:

Leaves are designed to harvest the light energy with their chloroplasts located in the photosynthetic cells. A cross section of a leaf is shown below. Photosynthesis generally occurs in mesophyll cells containing abundant chloroplasts. There are approximately 50 million chloroplasts per cm^2 in an actively growing green leaf. The light reactions (converting light energy into chemical energy -NADPH) occur on the thylakoid membranes and the protons are pumped from the stroma into the thylakoid space. When they return to the stroma, protons help ATP synthesis (photophosphorylation). The ATPs and NADPH are used to fix CO_2. CO_2 enters the leaf through stomatal pores and is converted to carbohydrates in the stroma. The carbohydrates made in the stroma are transported into large veins via smaller veins; both large and small veins contain phloem to transport sugars to other parts of the plant for use or storage. Xylem elements in veins help transport water and minerals.

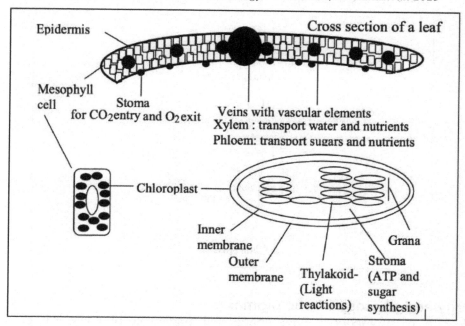

B. Basic Reactions:

In photosynthesis all the reactions may be summarized as follows.

$$6\ CO_2 + 12\ H_2O + Light \rightarrow C_6H_{12}O_6 + 6\ O_2 + 6\ H_2O$$

This summary reaction occurs in several steps in several parts of chloroplast. This can be simplified even further as

$$CO_2 + H_2O + Light \rightarrow CH_2O + O_2$$

Using radioactive oxygen (^{18}O), research has shown that the O_2 evolved (released) from the photosynthesis reaction comes from the splitting of a water molecule. The release of O_2 occurs during the light reactions to replenish the 2 electrons lost from photosystem II (see details later). CO_2 is fixed into carbohydrates during Calvin Cycle (AKA light -independent) reactions. Photosynthesis is a reductive and endergonic biosynthesis process involving $NADP^+$ (nicotinamide adenine dinucleotide phosphate) as the electron carrier. $NADP^+$ receives electrons from the light reactions and transfers them to Calvin cycle to generate carbohydrates.

Photophosphorylation: Electron transfer through a series of thylakoid membrane proteins results in the generation of a proton gradient inside the thylakoid, which becomes acidic. When protons return to the stroma through ATP synthase, they help in the synthesis of ATP, as in the chemiosmosis of respiration.

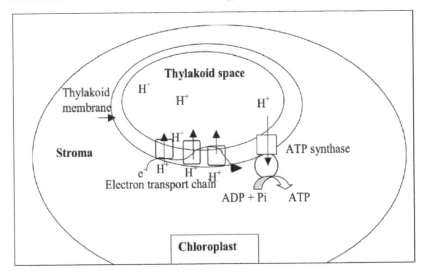

C. Light energy and photosynthetic pigments:

Sunlight is a form of electromagnetic wave energy with particulate photons. It is emitted from fusion reactions occurring in the sun. The energy of photons is inversely proportional to their wavelengths (distance between the two crests of electromagnetic waves). The wavelengths of the visible light range from 380 nm to 750 nm consisting of violet, indigo, blue, green, orange and red colors (VIBGYOR). Green is the least effective because most of it is reflected or transmitted (that is why most plants look green). Blue and red are the most effective because chlorophyll and other pigments absorb maximum light in these wavelength ranges.

A **photosystem** is a light harvesting complex and it includes the following components

1. Chlorophyll *a, b* and other pigments to absorb light.
2. Reaction center - specialized chlorophyll *a* molecules to emit excited electrons.
3. The primary electron acceptor

Leaves contain photosynthetic pigments such as chlorophyll *a*, chlorophyll *b*, beta-carotene and phycocyanin. The pigments contain a porphyrin ring with Mg^{2+} in the middle and a long hydrocarbon chain, which anchors them on the thylakoid membrane. These pigments absorb light at a specific wavelength range (shown by **the absorption spectrum)** with a defined peak (the maximum absorption). Photons are absorbed by these pigments and converted into chemical energy within a range of wavelengths **(shown by action spectrum)**, which may be different from the absorption spectrum.

Photosynthetic pigments are located around the reaction centers containing two chlorophyll-a molecules. When various pigments receive photons of a specific wavelength, they pass on that energy to reaction center chlorophyll. A pair of electrons in the reaction center chlorophyll is excited to a higher energy level, proportional to the energy level of the photons received. The excited electrons are absorbed by primary electron acceptor proteins and go through a series of membrane proteins comprising the electron transport chain, resulting in ATP and NADPH synthesis.

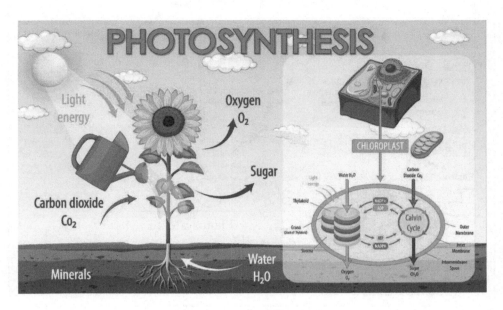

II.   LIGHT REACTIONS

The light reactions (light-dependent reactions) occur on the thylakoid membrane, containing photosystems I and II, which harvest light energy to generate ATP and NADPH in the stroma.

There are two types of photosystems as shown below.

Photosystem I (PS I)	**Photosystem II (PS II)**
Reaction center chl-a absorbs light with 700 nm peak	Reaction center chl a absorbs light with 680 nm peak
Reduces $NADP^+$ to NADPH in non-cyclic photophosphorylation ATP synthesis	Water is split into $2 H^+$, $2 e^-$ and $1/2 O_2$. ATP synthesis
Present in both cyclic and non-cyclic photophosphorylation.	Functions in only non-cyclic photophosphorylation

The excited electrons are transferred in two different ways in non-cyclic and cyclic photophosphorylation with different results. The non-cyclic is the primary mechanism in photosynthesis and cyclic occurs when there is not enough $NADP^+$ are available.

Non-cyclic Photophosphorylation

In non-cyclic photophosphorylation both PS I and PS II are involved. The electrons do not return to the starting place (reaction center) and end up in NADPH. The electrons lost by the PS II after receiving photons are replaced by extracting electrons from the splitting of water. The excited electrons from the PS II reaction center are accepted by the primary electron acceptor, transferred to pheophytin (Ph or I; an oxidizing agent), plastoquinone, the cytochrome complex and plastocyanin and finally to the PS I reaction center which had earlier lost excited electrons to its primary electron acceptor. The electrons lost by PS II are replaced by the splitting of water molecules into oxygen, protons and electrons. O_2 is released from PS II long before CO_2 is fixed into sugars. The oxygen-releasing plants evolved later and made our atmosphere rich in O_2 suitable for other aerobic organisms. The electrons from PS I are transferred to a membrane bound ferredoxin, a soluble ferredoxin and finally are used to reduce $NADP^+$ to generate NADPH. ATP is generated during the electron transfer from PS II to PS I.

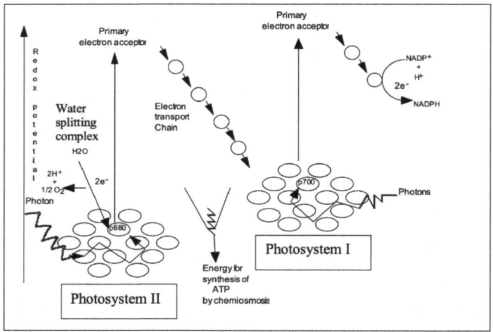

The products of the light reactions such as ATP and NADPH, generated in the stroma are used in the Calvin cycle (see the table below), to fix CO_2 into carbohydrates.

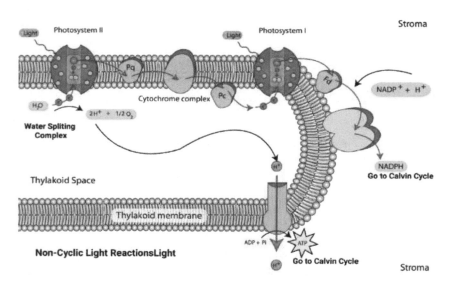

ATP is hydrolyzed into ADP; and NADPH is oxidized to $NADP^+$ during the Calvin cycle. These return to the light reactions to be converted again into ATP and NADPH, respectively.

Cyclic Photophosphorylation

The excited electrons from the PS I reaction center are received by the primary electron acceptor and transferred to ferredoxin (Fd; a protein), plastoquinone (PQ; an organic molecule), cytochrome (Cyt; a protein complex), plastocyanin (PC; a reducing agent) and finally back to the photosystem I reaction center. The electron transport is utilized to create a proton gradient to drive ATP synthesis.

During the cyclic photophosphorylation, water is not split, oxygen is not evolved and NADPH is not made.

This process occurs in primitive plants and when no NADPH is needed (i.e. in a high $NADPH/NADP^+$ ratio environment).

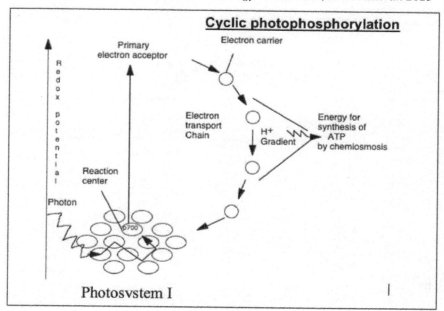

Cyclic electron transfer	Non-cyclic electron transfer
Involves only PS I	Use both PS I and PS II
Electrons return to PS I reaction center.	Electrons do not return to reaction center
ATP synthesized in PS I	ATP synthesized in PS II
No NADPH made	Electrons are used to reduce $NADP^+$ to generate NADPH
No O_2 is evolved	O_2 is evolved from the splitting of water
Electron recycled	The ultimate electron source is H_2O
Occurs wl......Photosystem I.....s high	Most common in plants

III.   CALVIN CYCLE

These reactions are light independent i.e., can occur in dark or light. However, they need the ATP and NADPH produced in the light reactions. These reactions are called the Calvin-Benson cycle or simply Calvin cycle, named after its discoverers, Melvin Calvin and Andrew Benson. It is also called C_3 cycle because CO_2 is first fixed into a 3-C compound. The three major stage of Calvin cycle are carbon fixation, reduction and regeneration of RuBP. The steps involved in the cycle are summarized below.

Remember only the step 1 (key step) and the summary of the Calvin cycle. The numbers of molecules are not critical.

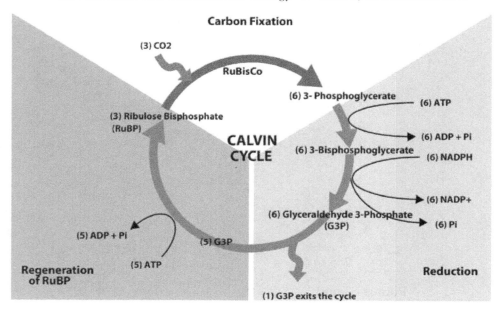

Calvin cycle

Carbon Fixation Reactions

Step 1. CO_2 is combined with a 5-C compound ribulose bisphosphate (RuBP) to generate two 3-C compounds 3-phosphoglycerate by the enzyme ribulose bisphosphate carboxylase/oxygenase (rubisco).

$$3\,(CO_2) + 3\,(\text{ribulose bisphosphate}) \xrightarrow[\text{Rubisco}]{} 6\,(\text{3-phosphoglycerate})$$

This is a key regulatory step of the C_3 cycle controlling the synthesis of sugars by CO_2 fixation. The regulation is explained later in the chapter.

Reduction Reactions:

Step 2. Phosphorylation of 3-phosphoglycerate into 1,3-bisphospho-glycerate by phosphoglycerate kinase.

$$6\,(\text{3-phosphoglycerate}) \xrightarrow[]{6\,ATP \quad 6\,ADP} 6\,(\text{1,3-bisphosphoglycerate})$$

This is the first step in the C_3 cycle to use ATPs generated in the light reaction.

Step 3. 1,3-bisphosphoglycerate is dephosphorylated and reduced to glyceraldehyde 3-phosphate. The high energy 1-phosphate and the reducing power of NADPH obtained from the light reactions are used here.

$$6\,(\text{1,3-bisphosphoglycerate}) \xrightarrow[]{6\,NADPH \quad 6\,NADP^+ + 6\,Pi} 6\,(\text{Glyceraldehyde 3-phosphate})$$

Glyceraldehyde 3-phosphate dehydrogenase.

Step 4. The synthesis of glucose and other carbohydrates takes place from 1 out of 6 molecules of glyceraldehyde 3-phosphate through several steps. You need two sets of reactions described above to generate one hexose. These steps resemble the reverse of glycolysis to generate 6-C sugars from 3-C sugars.

$$(\text{Glyceraldehyde 3-phosphate}) \longrightarrow \longrightarrow \text{glucose + other sugars.}$$

100

Sucrose and starch are the major forms of storage carbohydrates in plants.

Regeneration of RuBP

Step 5. Regeneration of ribulose bisphophate to continue the cycle. Five glyceraldehyde 3-phosphate (3-C) are used in a series of steps to regenerate 3 molecules of ribulose bisphosphate (5-C). This goes to step 1 to fix another 3 CO_2 molecules to generate 6 3-C sugars. Some more ATPs are used in these steps to generate RuBP.

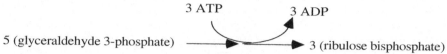

$$3\ ATP \qquad\qquad 3\ ADP$$

5 (glyceraldehyde 3-phosphate) $\longrightarrow$ 3 (ribulose bisphosphate)

Regulation of Rubisco

Rubisco (RuBP carboxylase and oxygenase) is probably the most abundant protein on earth, for up to 50% of a leaf's soluble protein is rubisco. It is made up of 8 large subunits of 55 kDa each and 8 small subunits of 15 kDa, each making the whole enzyme complex of approximately 560 kDa in size. The large subunit is the catalytic subunit and it is made in the chloroplast. The small subunit is the regulatory subunit generated in the cytoplasm and imported into the chloroplast. Rubisco can fix both CO_2 (carboxylase) and O_2 (oxygenase) into RuBP. Fixing O_2 into RuBP is called photorespiration which will be explained later.

Rubisco is regulated by the following factors:
1. *Concentration of CO_2 and O_2 in the cell.* Since rubisco can fix both CO_2 and O_2 , it is sensitive to their concentration. When the level of CO_2 goes down after intense light and Calvin cycle, rubisco starts to fix oxygen and release CO_2 during photorespiration.
2. *Mg^{2+} concentration.* Mg^{2+} is needed for the activity of Rubisco. The level of Mg^{2+} increases in the stroma upon illumination to facilitate carbon fixation.
3. *pH.* When the light reactions are in operation, the pH in the stroma increases from 7 to 8 which is the optimal pH of rubisco.
4. *NADPH levels.* The activity of rubisco is stimulated by greater levels of NADPH generated during the light reactions.

Photorespiration:

On hot, sunny and dry days, when the stomatal pores in leaves are closed to conserve moisture, the CO_2 intensity falls to a low level, concomitant with the rise of O_2; and rubisco starts to fix O_2 into RuBP in a series of reactions that finally releases CO_2. This process of fixing O_2 and releasing CO_2 in light is called photorespiration. This process results in the use of RuBP without making any sugars or ATP. This process occurs until the CO_2 levels are back to normal within the cell.

IV.   VARIATIONS OF CALVIN CYCLE

A. C3 plants: Only the Calvin cycle is used to fix CO_2. The majority of plants are C3. The C3 pathway evolved earlier than C4 or CAM pathways. Examples of C3 plants are rice and wheat.

B. C4 plants: Uses both C3 and C4 pathways

Plants have developed alternative strategies to overcome photorespiration and maximize CO_2 fixation using another pathway called the C4 pathway. This pathway involves an enzyme called phosphoenolpyruvate carboxylase (PEP carboxylase) which fixes CO_2 into 4-C sugars (hence the name C4 pathway). PEP carboxylase has no affinity for O_2 and so even when the CO_2 levels go down during the hot sunny weather, the CO_2 fixation continues and photorespiration is minimized. The C4 plants utilize both C3 and C4 pathways to fix CO_2. In C4 plants, the C3 pathway is limited to bundle sheath cells (cells adjacent to veins) and the C4 pathway is limited to mesophyll cells (closer to the surface). Corn and sugarcane are examples of two important C4 plants. The C4 plants are efficient in CO_2 fixation and water use efficiency.

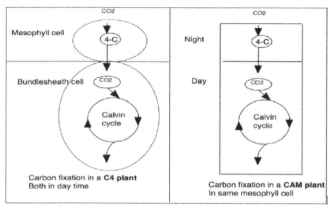

C. CAM plants

Crassulacean Acid Metabolism was first discovered in the family Crassulaceae. These plants also operate both C3 and C4 cycles to fix CO_2 into 4-C sugars first and thereafter into 3-C sugars. The major difference between C4 and CAM plants is that CAM plants do not have separate cells for C3 and C4 pathways. Instead, CAM plants carry out the C3 reactions during the day time (when stomata are closed during the hot sunny weather and ATP and NADPH are available) and the C4 reactions during the night time (when stomata are open in the cooler weather and CO_2 is available) e.g. pineapple, cacti. Many succulent desert plants use this strategy to fix CO_2.

Summary

Photosynthesis involves light reactions to generate ATP and NADPH which are used in Calvin cycle to fix CO_2 into 3-carbon (C3 plant) or 4-carbon (C4 and CAM plants) sugars, which eventually become hexose and polysaccharides. Carbohydrates are the major source of energy and provide carbon-skeletons to generate other organic products. During the light reactions, O_2 is evolved, enriching the atmosphere with O_2 available for respiration. Thus, photosynthesis is vital for the existence of almost all the living organisms in the world.

12. LIPID METABLISM

Concepts:

- Lipids include a diverse group of molecules, most of which are non-polar hydrocarbons
- Lipids store far more energy per gram compared to carbohydrates or proteins.
- Fats are made up of fatty acids and glycerol. The fatty acids are built from the units of acetyl CoA.
- Steroids such as cholesterol, estradiol and testosterone and the pigments carotenoids are made from isoprene (a 5-carbon molecule) units.
- Fats are broken down by a process called ☐-oxidation to release acetyl CoA and NADH.

Outline
I. Overview of lipids
II. Biosynthesis of lipids
III. Catabolism of lipids

I Overview of Lipids

Lipids are small biological molecules found in many organisms and compounds. They usually comprise of a polar head group and non-polar tail. However, the non-polar tail is much larger than the polar head, resulting in lipids being very **hydrophobic** (water-fearing) and overall non-polar. Because of their non-polar and hydrophobic nature, the vast majority of association between lipids occurs via an entropy-driven hydrophobic effect. Additionally, lipid association is stabilized through Van der Waals interactions between the hydrophobic groups of the lipid biomolecules. Some commonly found lipids are triglycerides, fats (saturated and unsaturated), phospholipids, carotenoids, and steroids.

Lipids are major energy-storage molecules. They can store up to 9 Calories of energy per gram of fat. They are better in storing energy than carbohydrates for two reasons. First, they are able to pack together more tightly than carbohydrates can pack (due to their hydrophobic nature) and thus you have more carbons per unit area than carbohydrates. Second, fats are more reduced than carbohydrates and thus have more energy in each carbon-carbon than carbohydrates. Lipids can also serve as insulation against heat loss (very valuable in cold weather) and can cushion vital organs. Lipids also serve as vitamins, pigments (think chlorophyll), growth hormones, and regulators. Finally, phospholipids make up a very large portion of the lipid bilayer of biological membranes.

II Fatty Acid Biosynthesis

Most animals and humans consume food in the form of carbohydrates. However, carbohydrate reserves in the bodies of living organisms are limited so the majority of ingested carbohydrate is converted into fat and stored as energy in fat reserves.

A central precursor for fatty acid synthesis is **Acetyl-CoA.** The acetyl-CoA used in fatty acid synthesis comes from two major sources- the beta oxidation of fatty acids and from pyruvate in the pyruvate dehydrogenase complex (recall this step following glycolysis in respiration). Thus, Acetyl-CoA is cycling back from both the breakdown of fatty acids and carbohydrates.

It is important to note that although many living organisms can create fatty acids from carbohydrates the reverse does not occur. That is, animals cannot synthesize carbohydrates from fatty acids due to the irreversible nature of the pyruvate dehydrogenase complex.

Synthesis of Malonyl-CoA

The first committed step of fatty acid synthesis is the synthesis of Malonyl-CoA from Acetyl-CoA and carbonate. Like many other irreversible reactions, this reaction is coupled with ATP hydrolysis to make it very exergonic, and thus, virtually irreversible. Because it is irreversible, this step is a rate-limiting step. Finally, biotin is required as a cofactor for this reaction to proceed.

$$CH_3 - \overset{O}{\overset{||}{C}} - SCoA + HCO_3^- \xrightarrow[\text{acetyl CoA carboxylase}]{ATP \quad \nearrow^{ADP + Pi}} {}^-OOC - CH_2 - \overset{O}{\overset{||}{C}} - SCoA$$

acetyl CoA   malonyl CoA

All of the intermediates in fatty acid synthesis must be activated before partaking in any of the reactions in the biosynthesis pathway. These intermediates are activated by a small protein called **acyl carrier protein (ACP)**. The acyl groups of the intermediates are anchored to the CoA of ACP via a thioester linkage. ACP is part of the **fatty acid synthase (FAS)** complex. FAS is a long polypeptide chain that has many domains. Each of its domains is utilized in a step of the fatty acid synthesis process.

Stepwise Reactions in Fatty Acid Synthesis Following Malonyl-CoA Formation
1. An acetyl group is transferred from Acetyl-CoA to ACP via the enzyme **Acetyl-CoA ACP transacylase**.
2. The acyl (acetyl+ACP) group gets transferred to the FAS complex.
3. The malonyl group from Malonyl-CoA is also transferred to the FAS complex via the enzyme **Malonyl-CoA ACP transacylase**. Now we have both a malonyl and the acyl group in the FAS complex and these combine to form acyl-malonyl-ACP.
4. The carboxyl group is removed (as carbon dioxide) from malonyl-ACP and the acetyl group is transferred to malonyl-ACP resulting in a final product of **3-keto acyl ACP**.
5. The 3-keto group then undergoes a reduction reaction, followed by a dehydration reaction, followed by a second reduction reaction to create CH_2. The two reduction reactions require the cofactor **NADPH**.

This first cycle of fatty acid synthesis results in a 4-carbon compound in the FAS in the ACP arm (one of the domains of the FAS). It gets transferred to the K arm (another domain of the FAS) and another malonyl-CoA is brought into the ACP arm and the cycle begins again. For each malonyl-CoA introduced into the FAS complex, and thus for each cycle, the fatty acid chain is extended by two carbons. At the end of 7 cycles, a 16-carbon chain is extending from the ACP of the FAS. The FAS cannot synthesize fatty acids longer than 16 carbons, thus when there is a 16-carbon chain, the link between the fatty acid chain and the ACP arm is hydrolyzed, yielding **palmitic acid**, a 16-carbon fatty acid.

Net Reaction:
Acetyl CoA + 7 malonyl CoA + 14 NADPH + 14 H^+ → Palmitate + 7 CO_2 + 8 CoA + 14 $NADP^+$ +6H_2O

Modification of Palmitic Acid
For palmitic acid to be modified, it needs to first be converted into palmityl CoA. Once it is converted into palmityl CoA, carbons are added two at a time by adding malonyl-CoA. If an unsaturated fatty acid needs to be produced, enzymes called fatty acid CoA desaturases add double bonds. Ease desaturase adds a double bond at a specific place.

III Steroid Biosynthesis

Steroids are an important class of lipids and can serve as hormones and vitamins amongst other things. We will now look at the closely at the biosynthesis of cholesterol.

The precursor for the synthesis of cholesterol is **hydroxymethylglutaryl-coenzyme A** (HMG-CoA). This molecule is formed by the condensation of acetyl-CoA and acetoacetyl-CoA and is catalyzed by the enzyme **HMG-CoA synthase.** Next, HMG-CoA reductase catalyzes the production of **mevalonate** from HMG-CoA. This step uses up two NADPH molecules and is the <u>rate-limiting step</u> of cholesterol synthesis. Thus, the enzyme that catalyzes this step (HMG-CoA reductase) is highly regulated.

isoprene

Mevalonate is then phosphorylated twice, in two steps using 2 ATPs, and the resulting molecule is decarboxylated (again using ATP) to yield isopentenyl pyrophosphate (IPP). IPP is one of the many **isoprenoids** in this pathway. Isoprenoids are a diverse class of lipids that are derived from 5-carbon isoprene units. They are precursors to the formation of steroids, responsible for the pigmentation in tomatoes, and the flavor of cinnamon, amongst many other roles. Another molecule that is synthesized from mevalonate is dimethylallyl pyrophosphate (DMAPP). Together, DMAPP and IPP are used to make much more complex isoprenoids such as steroid hormones, cholesterol, and vitamin K.

Isoprene unit made up of 5 carbons is the building block of many lipids including carotenoids, terpenes, essential oils etc.

Carotenoids shown on the next page are also made from isoprene units. These are 40 carbon long molecules built by combining 8 isoprene units

In addition to these lipids, there are a wide variety of molecules such as waxes, essential oils and many lipid-soluble vitamins that come under lipids.

IV Catabolism of Lipids

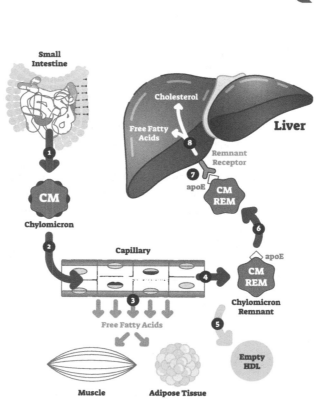

The lipids (primarily fats, i.e. triglycerides) ingested through food are mixed with bile salts in the small intestine and become micelles. The enzyme, lipase then breaks down the fats into fatty acids and glycerol. The mixture of fatty acids, some tri- or diglycerides along with dietary cholesterol enter the blood stream and distributed to the rest of the body for further catabolism.

Oxidation of glycerol and fatty acids

Fatty acids, especially saturated fatty acids, are transported into and broken down in the *mitochondrial matrix* in a process called **β-oxidation**. In addition, fatty acid oxidation can also occur in the peroxisomes of all eukaryotes and glyoxysomes in plants. Glycerol will be phosphorylated to make glycerol 3-phosphate and enters glycolysis to make ATP.

In order for fatty acids to undergo **β-** oxidation they must first be activated by binding the fatty acid to Coenzyme A (CoA). This binding is catalyzed by **fatty acyl-CoA ligases** and coupled with ATP hydrolysis making the overall activation exergonic.

Following the activation and initial beta oxidation the fatty acid is broken down two carbons at a time (in the form of acetyl-CoA) in a cyclic series of four steps.

The Steps of β-Oxidation

1) Initial dehydrogenation: Catalyzed by the enzyme **fatty acyl-CoA dehydrogenase**, results in the formation of a double bond between the α- and β- carbons of the acyl CoA. Results in reduction of FAD to $FADH_2$.

2) Hydration: Catalyzed by **enoyl-CoA hydratase**. The β-carbon has a hydroxyl group added to it. The -OH is obtained from H_2O.

3) Dehydrogenation: Catalyzed by **3-hydroxyacyl-CoA dehydrogenase**. Results in formation of double bond between β- carbon and oxygen (from -OH bond). Results in reduction of NAD^+ to NADH

4) Thiolytic cleavage: Catalyzed by **thiolase.** The bond between the α and β carbons is broken releasing Acetyl-CoA.

5) The acetyl CoA mainly enters the Krebs cycle for further oxidation and generation of limited amounts of ATP and a lot of NADH and $FADH_2$. The carbons are released as CO_2. The NADH and $FADH_2$ will enter oxidative phosphorylation to make a lot of ATP in the mitochondrion.

6) Some of the acetyl CoA will be converted into ketone bodies (acetone and acetoacetate) in the liver and are exported to other parts of the body. Acetone made in smaller amounts would be exhaled and other ketones are utilized for further catabolism and energy synthesis.

Cholesterol uptake and break down

Cholesterol molecules are sterols that are not soluble in water and hence carried in the blood through protein complexes knows as LDL- (low density lipoprotein) and HDL- (high density lipoprotein) Cholesterol. Cholesterol is made by liver and also taken through diet. Cholesterol is an essential component of cell membrane that affects the fluidity and permeability of membranes. The LDL and HDL-cholesterol are taken in from the blood stream through receptor mediated endocytosis and ingested into the cells for further break down.

Once the LDL- or HDL-cholesterol is inside the cell, as a food vesicle after the receptor mediated endocytosis, the vesicle fuses with lysosome to break down the lipids, proteins and releases cholesterol inside the cell. This cholesterol is then converted to esters and either excreted or recirculated inside the body. Cholesterol biosynthesis is complex and energy intensive process. Hence cholesterol synthesis is regulated by a key enzyme, HMG-CoA Reductase the target of many cholesterol-lowering medication such as Lipitor or other statins.

13. CELL DIVISION

Concepts
1. Cell division is essential for reproduction, repair, growth and development.
2. Bacterial cells divide by a simple process called binary fission.
3. Eukaryotic somatic cells undergo cell cycle that includes mitosis as the cell division process.
4. Cell cycle stages and reproduction are tightly regulated by proteins and environmental conditions.
5. Sexual reproduction needs two gametes each of which contain half the number of chromosomes so that when two gametes fertilize, the original chromosome number is regained and maintained in the resulting organism.
6. Meiosis occurs only to make reproductive cells or gametes in the male and female reproductive organs. Meiosis involves two cell division but with only one DNA replication.
7. Meiosis and random fertilization result in genetic variation among sexually reproduced organisms.

Outline
I. Bacterial reproduction - binary fission
II. Mitosis - somatic cell division
III. Regulation of cell division
IV. Meiosis and causes of genetic variation

Cell division is a very important process in every organism to replicate life, grow and develop, repair damaged organs and protect living cells. Prokaryotes, unicellular and multicellular eukaryotes such as plants and animals divide and undergo cell division in their own unique way. The common aspects in all cell divisions are DNA replication and division of other parts of the cell in an approximately equal manner. The cell division processes in bacteria, animals and plants are explained in this chapter.

I. BACTERIAL REPRODUCTION BY BINARY FISSION

Prokaryotes such as bacteria and archaebacteria divide by **binary fission**. The basic genetic elements of a bacterial cell, as shown in the Figure below, include the following:

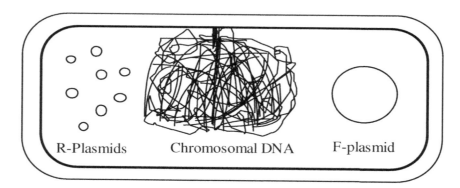

a. **Plasmid DNA**: Plasmids are extra chromosomal circular DNA molecules. Each plasmid contains an origin of replication (a specific region of DNA recognized by DNA replication enzymes) and genes coding for antibiotic resistance or enzymes to make specific nutrients. These plasmids vary in their size (ranging from 3 to 140 kilo base pairs) and in the number of genes they carry. They replicate independent of the chromosomal DNA. The different types of plasmids and their broad range of functions are given below.

R-plasmids: These are the plasmids containing antibiotic resistance genes. These are the genes that allow some disease causing bacteria to develop resistance against commonly used antibiotics.

F-plasmids: These are fertility plasmids which contain genes for making F-pili (reproductive part to transmit DNA during bacterial mating). F-plasmids are transmitted through sexual mating.

C-factors: Colicinogenic factors contain genes coding for toxins, important for the survival of the bacteria.

b. Chromosomal DNA: Bacterial cells contain long (~ 5,000 kb) circular chromosomal DNA. Each cell contains a single origin of replication and it is bound to the plasma membrane. Unlike eukaryotic chromosomes, their DNA is not bound by any protein envelope. The DNA is confined to a region called the nucleoid region. The chromosomal DNA replicates once per cell division. It replicates while it is attached to the plasma membrane. The plasmids replicate independent of the bacterial cell division.

Binary Fission

Once a bacterium replicates its chromosomal DNA with a sufficient number of plasmid DNA and other cell contents, the plasma membrane grows inward to divide the cell in two. A new cell wall is formed between the two daughter cells. Each of the daughter cells has one copy of chromosomal DNA, a random number of plasmid DNA and other components of the cell.

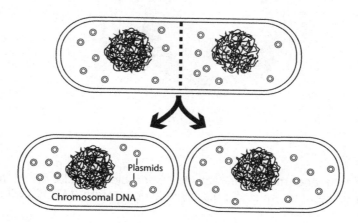

This process is called **binary fission.** Bacteria such as *Escherichia coli* divide approximately once every 20 minutes. The plasmid DNA replicates independently many times during the life cycle of bacteria.

Chloroplasts and mitochondria also replicate by binary fission during the life cycle of eukaryotic cells as they are considered prokaryotic in nature.

II. MITOSIS – SOMATIC CELL DIVISION

Mitosis is the process by which eukaryotic cells replicate their DNA into two identical copies and divide to form two identical cells. All somatic- and vegetative cells divide by mitosis. Identical twins and clones are produced by mitosis.

A. Genetic elements of eukaryotic cells:

Eukaryotic cells have linear chromosomes, which are organized into chromatin (DNA + protein loosely dispersed in the nucleus) in actively growing cells. The chromosomal DNA is bound to the histone group of proteins DNA is wound around histones to form nucleosomes (small beads of DNA and histones) and condensed nucleosomes form the looped domains of chromatin. The looped domains condense to form chromosomes during the metaphase stage of cell division. Chromatin is made up of approximately 35% DNA, 60% proteins and 5% RNA. Genes are defined by specific DNA sequences in the chromosomes and may encode different kinds of RNA and a large variety of proteins.

Once a chromosomes is replicated, (making two identical copies), the two strands are attached at the center and the two strands of this chromosome are called sister chromatids. It is still considered as a single chromosome. The central region of the attachment is called the **centromere** and the ends of the chromosomes, called the **telomeres**. Since the eukaryotic chromosomes are large, they may have multiple origins of replication at which the DNA replicating enzymes bind to initiate the DNA replication.

All somatic cells of a species have the same number of chromosomes. The number is unique to that particular species. The reproductive cells (gametes) contain half that number. Higher eukaryotes do not have plasmids but some fungi may contain plasmids. Organelles such as chloroplasts and mitochondria contain their own chromosomes, which are similar to prokaryotic chromosomes (circular DNA) and these organelles replicate on their own by binary fission.

B. Cell cycle:

Cell cycle consists of two major phases, namely, interphase and mitotic (M) phase. Interphase is divided into G1, S and G2 phases. Mitotic phase is divided into prophase, prometaphase, metaphase, anaphase and telophase & cytokinesis.

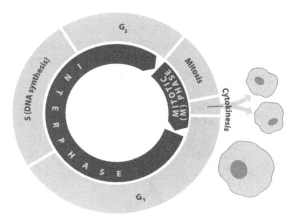

1. Interphase:

G1 (Gap 1): Rapid growth and metabolic activity. Centrioles, made up of microtubules, replicate. Centrioles occur in the middle of the microtubule organizing centers (MTOC) with microtubules radiating from the center.

S-phase (DNA Synthesis): Chromosomes replicate along with their proteins but are still loosely dispersed as chromatin. The replicated DNA is identical to the parental chromosome. The individual strands of chromosomes are called sister chromatids which remain attached at the centromere region.

G2 (Gap 2): Growth and final preparation phase: All organelles and membranes are duplicated throughout interphase. Chloroplasts and mitochondria also have replicated by binary fission.

2. M-phase: Mitosis + cytokinesis:

Mitosis occurs in 4 distinct phases: prophase, metaphase, anaphase and telophase, followed by cytokinesis.

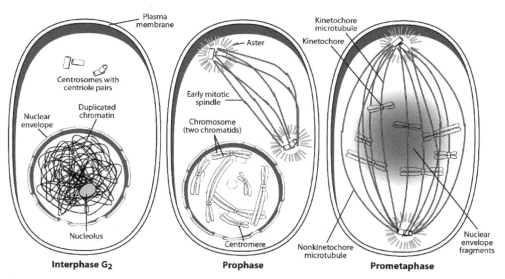

Prophase: This phase is sometimes divided into prophase and prometaphase. In prophase all the preparation for cell division occurs. In the nucleus, the nucleolus disappears; the chromatin gets denser and forms chromatids. The two pairs of centrioles (asters) move to opposite poles. In the cytoplasm, the mitotic spindle (made up of microtubules) forms from the MTOC (in plants) or centrioles (in animals).

Prometaphase, the nuclear envelope fragments and disappears. Microtubules of spindle fibers (polar fibers) are connected to the chromosomes at places called the kinetochore (15-35 microtubules per kinetochore). The fibers attached at this place are called the kinetochore fibers and others are called non-kinetochore fibers. The structure with two sister chromatids attached to a centromere, is still considered a single chromosome.

Metaphase: The sister chromatids of replicated chromosomes are aligned in the middle of the cell. It is called the metaphase plate. This is the final preparation before the chromatids separate.

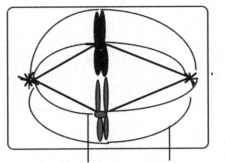

kinetochore-fibers   Non-kinetochore fibers

Anaphase: The centromere of each chromosome divides to initiate anaphase. Each of the daughter chromatids after separation is now called a chromosome. The two newly formed chromosomes (earlier called chromatids) move apart to separate the sister chromatids into 2 single stranded chromosomes. Chromosomes move approximately at 1 µm/sec due to depolymerization of microtubules near the kinetochore to bring the chromosomes closer to poles. No ATP is needed for this process.

Telophase: Polar fibers elongate by adding more microtubules (polymerization) using ATP to expand the cell more. The two new nuclei form to envelope the two new groups of daughter chromosomes. Nucleoli reappear inside each nucleus. The chromosomes loosen to become chromatin again.

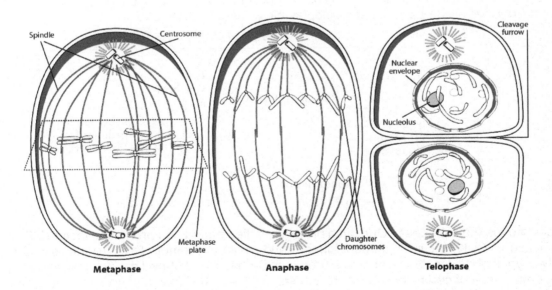

Cytokinesis: The cytoplasm furrows inward in the case of animal cells making a **cleavage furrow. I**n the case of the plant cell, a **cell plate** forms to divide the two daughter cells, each with its nucleus, chromosomes, organelles etc. The cells will enter into interphase again to grow and develop or divide again. The resulting cells are identical in the DNA content and number of chromosomes. All the cells in the body other than reproductive cells divide through mitosis.

Many organisms that reproduce vegetatively only use mitosis to divide and differentiate. The possibility of cloning animals from an embryonic cell or totipotent somatic cell is possible because of mitosis resulting in identical progeny. Naturally the identical twins are formed due to the mitotic division of the zygote after fertilization in the uterus. After the mitotic division, the two identical cells continue to divide and develop as separate fetuses. The cell division in the somatic cells is a tightly controlled process as explained later in this chapter.

Summary of Mitosis

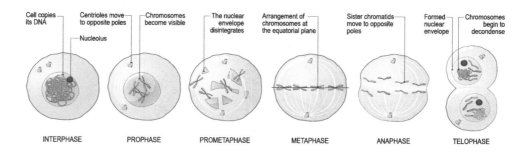

I.   Regulation of Cell Division

Cell division is a tightly controlled process in the cell. It is important to renew the cells and for development of new tissues or a whole new organism. Proteins and the genes coding for such proteins control checkpoints, rate and sequence. Nutritional status, growth factors, hormones, cell density and other environmental factors also influence the divisions.

Control of cell division is studied in cell culture growing in specialized medium, e.g. plant cell cultures such as maize and tobacco cell suspensions. In human cells, the cell lines are sometimes obtained from the cancer cells (immortalized cells). These animal cells are grown on monolayer or in suspensions to conduct experiments. The critical stage (restriction point) to control cell division is in the G1 phase from which the cells go to G0 (no more division as in nerve cells or muscle cells) or S-phase (synthetic), the G2 phase and the M phase. Cells divide based on the cytoplasmic volume to DNA ratio.

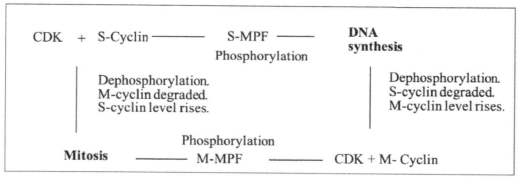

Proteins regulate the main process. One such protein is called maturation promoting factor (MPF). MPF is a combination of CDK (cyclin dependent kinase) and cyclin to promote DNA synthesis and mitosis. There are two types of cyclins: S-cyclin, which promotes S-phase, and M-cyclin which promotes M-phase. Depending on the level of cyclin concentration, it binds to CDK. The binding of cyclin to cdc-2 stimulates autophosphorylation of CDK (kinase) and phosphorylation of several other proteins involved in cell division. Some of those proteins are proteases, which can degrade cyclin to bring the levels down to regulate the cycle. The whole regulation is depicted in the figure below.

So, depending on the phosphorylation status of S-MPF and M-MPF, DNA synthesis or mitosis occurs.

III.   MEIOSIS AND SEXUAL REPRODUCTION

I.   Overview of sexual reproduction

Meiosis occurs in sex cells to generate reproductive cells (gametes) with half the number of chromosomes that are different, but derived from both the parent chromosomes. Meiosis is also known as reduction division. This is important for sexual reproduction where individual gametes from two parents (male and female) combine to form a new zygote cell developing into a new organism.

Ploidy level indicates how many sets of chromosomes (N) are present in   a cell as mentioned below.

Haploid (1N) single set of chromosomes. e.g. sperm cell, egg cell.
Diploid (2N) two sets of chromosomes. e.g. body cells
Tetraploid (4N) four sets of chromosomes. e.g. plants, tobacco.
Polyploid (manyN) several sets of chromosomes. e.g. sugarcane.

The basic differences between sexual and asexual reproduction are shown below.

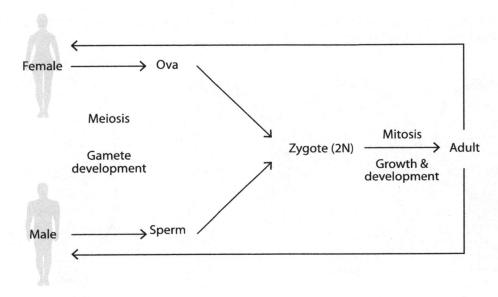

Example of a diploid cell:

Human cells contain 46 chromosomes or 23 pairs or two sets as in any other diploid organism. Among these 22 are called autosomes and two (X and Y) are sex chromosomes. The 23 pairs come from two parents. So in each pair of chromosome, one is paternal (from father) and another is maternal (from mother). These pairs are called **homologous chromosomes** or homologs (i.e. similar but not identical). Each homologous chromosome has equivalent copy or copies of a gene (coding for RNA or protein). These two forms of a gene are called **alleles**. During meiosis the chromosome number 46 in the diploid cell is halved into 23 chromosomes in the gametes.

Sexual Reproduction	Asexual Reproduction
Involves gametes or reproductive cells.	Involves somatic or vegetative cells.
Needs both meiosis and mitosis.	Mitosis is enough to reproduce.
Two parents/cells needed.	Single parent or cell is enough.
Chromosome number is reduced to half in gametes and then regained after fertilization.	Chromosomes numbers and DNA sequence remains same.

Greater variation among offspring due to recombination. e.g. animals, most plants	Highly homogeneous population due to identical progenies. E.g. potato, sugarcane.

II. Meiosis: Overview of meiotic cell division:

Meiosis I
Diploid cell (2N) → Interphase I (DNA replication) → Prophase I → Metaphase I → Anaphase I → Telophase I → Cytokinesis I → 2 daughter cells (recombined homologs separated but the sister chromotaids are still attached)

Meiosis II
Interphase II (No DNA replication) → Prophase II → Metaphase II → Anaphase II → Telophase II → Cytokinesis II →
4 haploid (1N) daughter cells (sister chromtids separated)

Meiosis I
During meiosis I, the chromosomes replicate, homologous chromosomes cross over to exchange genetic material, and the homologs separate.

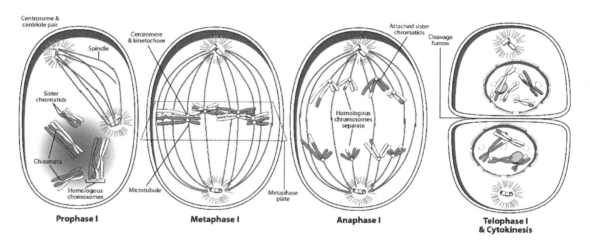

Prophase I | Metaphase I | Anaphase I | Telophase I & Cytokinesis

Interphase I:
Chromosomes replicate into two identical sister chromatids attached at centromere. The centrioles and other organelles also duplicate.

Prophase I:
It is the most important stage in meiosis. This stage alone is more complex and takes more time than the whole mitosis. It occupies about 90% of the time of meiosis. The condensed chromosome is attached to the nuclear envelope. The homologous chromosomes align themselves and come together to form bivalents or tetrads (four chromatids). Each gene is brought closer to its other counterpart (allele) in the other chromatids. This process is called synapsis. During synapsis sections of homologous chromosomes are exchanged (DNA from one homolog is cut and joined with another homolog after getting equivalent portion). The overlapping of homologous chromosomes is called crossing over and the DNA exchange is called recombination. The X-shaped regions of crossing over are called chiasmata. This results in genetic exchange between the maternal and paternal chromosomes. This is a major source of variation among offsprings in sexual reproduction. The sister chromatids are still attached at the centromere. In the later part of Prophase I, the nuclear membrane disappears, centrioles move apart, and spindle fibers form.

Metaphase I:
Bivalent chromosomes (tetrads) align themselves along the middle of the cell along the metaphase plate. The kinetochore fibers attached to the centromere of each pair of recombined sister chromatids point to one pole only. There is a random assortment of homologous chromosomes during this alignment. This

also contributes to genetic variation.

Anaphase I: Individual pairs of sister chromatids separate from each other and go to opposite poles. The sister chromatids are still attached to each other.

Telophase I and Cytokinesis I: After the sister chromatids move to opposite poles, nuclear envelope may form and the cleavage furrow deepens to divide the cell. In plant cells, the cell plate forms.

Interphase II or Interkinesis is sometimes seen but no DNA replication happens.

Meiosis II:

This is similar to mitosis without DNA replication. Sister chromatids separate during the Meiosis II.

Prophase II: If nucleus and nucleolus are present, they disappear and spindle fibers appear.

Metaphase II: The sister chromatids align on the metaphase plate. The kinetochore fibers pointing to opposite poles are attached at the centromere.

Anaphase II: Centromeres of the sister chromatids finally separate and individual chromosomes (1N) finally move towards opposite ends.

Telophase II and Cytokinesis II: Nuclei begin to form around the chromosomes. Cleavage furrow or cell plate separates the new daughter cells.

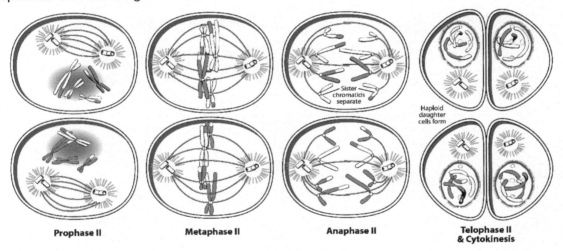

Prophase II   Metaphase II   Anaphase II   Telophase II & Cytokinesis

III Major sources of variation in sexual reproduction:
1. Crossing over during prophase I.
2. Independent assortment of chromosomes in metaphase I. If there are 23 pairs of chromosomes, there are 2^{23} (8.3886×10^6 or ~8 million) possible combinations.
3. Random fertilization. If each sperm and egg cell from two different parents has a random chance of combining, it means
$8.3886 \times 10^6 \times 8.3886 \times 10^6$ combinations, or 70.3686×10^{13}, or about seventy billion possible combinations for the offspring!

In addition to these variations, mutations accumulate in the DNA in both sexual and asexual reproduction.

Differences Between Mitosis and Meiosis

Mitosis	Meiosis
Chromosome number remains same.	Chromosome number is reduced to half.
Daughter cells genetically identical (2N).	Related but different (1N).
No synapsis, tetrads or crossing over.	Synapsis of tetrads leads to crossing over and recombination.
Sister chromatids separate during anaphase. Homologs also separate but each cell gets identical sets.	Homologs separate in anaphase I and sister chromatids separate in anaphase II.
One major division.	Two major divisions.
DNA replicate before each division.	DNA replicate before Meiosis I and not again before Meiosis II.
Two daughter cells.	Four daughter cells.

Concepts
1. Genes are units of inheritance as per Mendel and are passed on from one generation to next.
2. Alleles are alternate forms a gene and exists as pairs in diploid organisms.
3. There is no blending of traits from parents to offspring but discrete passing of specific genes corresponding to specific characteristic.
4. Some alleles are linked and some not unlinked in their inheritance pattern.

Outline
I. Basic genetic terms.
II. Mendel's laws of inheritance.
III. Complexities of genetic expression.
IV. Mendelian inheritance of human genetic disorders

I. BASIC GENETIC TERMS

Basic foundations of classical genetics were established by Johann Gregor Mendel with his papers published in 1866 which were recognized only in early 1900s. With the current knowledge of classical and molecular genetics (studied at DNA level) we can understand the basic mechanisms of inheritance much better than few decades ago. The relationship between some of the terms used in genetics can be summed up in this diagram.

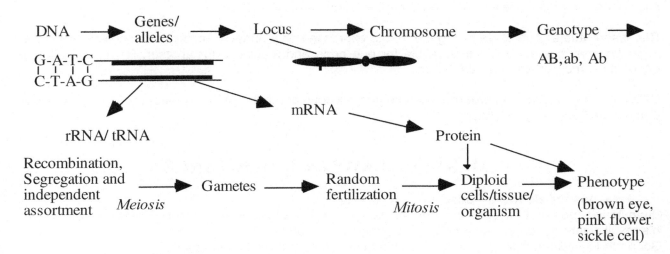

DNA: Deoxyribonucleic acid. The basic genetic material made of nucleic acid DNA present in each cell. DNA contains 4 nucleotides and encodes information to make RNA and protein. The basic details are explained in the chapter 5 on biological molecules and in chapter 16 on DNA structure.

Genes: According to classical genetics, gene is the unit of heredity. It is based on the expression of such a gene as a specific trait in the successive generations of an organism. These genes may not have been isolated and characterized. It is sometimes used to refer to a locus (see later). It is not exactly the same as in molecular genetics where gene is a particular DNA with a unique sequence which codes for a protein or RNA. Such genes may be 0.1 to 15 kilobases (kb) long.

Alleles: Alternate forms of a gene, responsible for a particular trait, present in two different chromosomes which are derived from mother and father. These alleles may code for the same protein with slightly different amino acid sequences, and hence may result in different traits. The alleles may be exchanged during meiosis in the crossing over and recombination process.

Locus: The location of a gene or few genes on a chromosome. (plural- loci). Sometimes it is used interchangeably with gene. Genes coding for different traits may exist close to each other on a locus. A locus may be as long as 50 to 100 kb consisting of several genes. Closely located genes within a locus are less likely to be separated from each other during recombination in meiosis. Hence they are sometimes referred to as closely linked genes/loci. The chromosomes are mapped with specific genes based on the frequency of recombination of known genes.

Chromosomes: contain several (hundreds of) loci each. Chromosomes exist as loosely dispersed chromatin (DNA + proteins) in interphase and condense during cell division. One can see the condensed chromosomes during the cell division. The chromosomes derived from father and mother (homologs) goes through genetic recombination in meiosis.

Genotype represents the assorted collection of various genes in the chromosomes. It is represented by capital or small letters of the notations for particular genes. e.g. AA, Aa, bb etc.

Phenotype refers to a physical trait, physiological condition or biochemical aspects which are determined by the genes at molecular level according to its genotype. E.g. eye color (physical), sickle cell anemia (physiological), herbicide resistant enzyme (biochemical).

Homozygous: An organism with a pair of identical alleles for a particular gene in both the homologous chromosomes. E.g. AA, aa, BB, bb.

Heterozygous: An organism with mixed allele pairs for a particular gene. An organism may be homozygous for one gene and heterozygous for another. E.g. Aa, Bb.

Dominant allele: The allele of a gene that is expressed under both homozygous and heterozygous condition. This is due to the DNA sequence of the particular gene and the nature of the protein coded by such gene. Dominant allele is denoted in capital letters. e.g. AA, BB, CC.

Recessive allele: The allele of a gene that is expressed only under homozygous condition. Again, an organism may contain a dominant allele for one gene and recessive for another. Recessive allele is denoted in small letters. E.g. aa, bb, cc.

Based on the genotype an organism can be homozygous dominant (AA) or homozygous recessive (aa) or it can be heterozygous (Aa).

II. MENDEL'S LAWS OF INHERITANCE

Reasons for Mendel's Success:
1. Quantitative approach. He used a mathematical approach to a biological problem. This is one reason why his results were not appreciated or acknowledged immediately.
2. Good model system. Peas are easy to grow and hybridize to monitor inheritance.
3. Selection of traits or phenotypes those are easy to study such as pod color (green/yellow), seed shape (round/wrinkled), stem length (tall/dwarf) etc. which is measurable and distinct.

Method: Pure bred (homozygous) varieties (parents) are crossed by hybridization (fertilizing one plant's stigma with another plant's pollen), observe the first generation (F1) and back cross the F1 with parents or self the F1 to study the segregation at second generation (F2)

A. Law of segregation.
Allele pairs segregate (separate) during gamete formation and the paired condition is restored by the random fusion of gametes at fertilization.

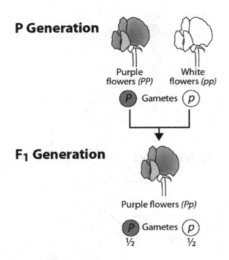

P Generation

Purple flowers *(PP)*   White flowers *(pp)*

P Gametes p

F₁ Generation

Purple flowers *(Pp)*

P Gametes p
½   ½

F₂ Generation

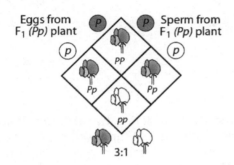

Eggs from F₁ *(Pp)* plant   Sperm from F₁ *(Pp)* plant

3:1

Example:

Mendel selected purebred pea varieties with either purple or white color flowers. When he crossed them and obtained first progenies (F1) all of which had purple flowers. He self-pollinated all of the F1 plants and found 3/4th of the F2 progenies had purple flowers and 1/4th had white flowers. The ratio was 3:1 for these two traits. This cross is called a monohybrid cross. From these results of restoring the white flower, he formulated the particulate theory of the "gene" as discrete units of heredity which separate during the formation of gametes and can be mixed by fertilizing two gametes to restore the phenotype. The units of heredity are present as alleles in the gametes which segregate during gamete formation and he demonstrated this by breeding the peas as shown in the figure on next page.

Test cross is done by hybridizing a parent with unknown genotype with a known homozygous recessive parent to find out if the unknown genotype is homozygous or heterozygous.

If the unknown parent is homozygous:

aa x <u>AA</u> = all F1 will be heterozygous (Aa).

If the unknown parent is heterozygous:

aa x <u>Aa</u> = half of F1 will be homozygous (aa) and other half heterozygous (Aa).

B. Law of independent assortment:

Law: The segregation of each allele pair is independent of other allele pairs. The individual allele pairs need to be located on separate loci, far from each other to allow independent assortment during gamete formation.

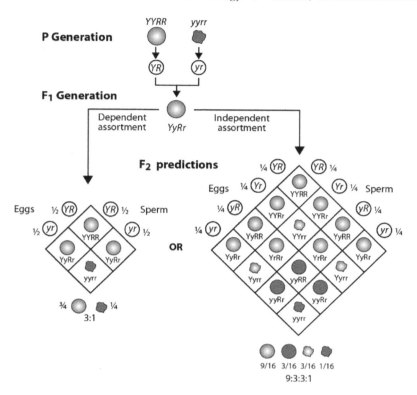

Example: This can be explained by considering two different traits coded by two allele pairs. This is referred to as a dihybrid cross. Round (R) and yellow (Y) seeds are dominant traits with their corresponding recessive alleles for dented (rr) and green (yy) seeds phenotype. If we cross a parent which is homozygous dominant for both (RRYY) with spherical yellow seeds with another parent which is homozygous recessive (rryy) for both alleles with dented green seeds, one can expect completely heterozygous condition (RrYy) with spherical yellow seeds in F1 generation. When these seeds are selfed, the following probabilities are observed as shown below.

These probabilities in a dihybrid cross can also be obtained by using the rule of multiplication (to determine the chances of two independent events occurring together).
Probabilities of a seed being
- yellow is 3/4 or round is 3/4, (because they are dominant traits   as we saw in monohybrid cross),
- both yellow and round is 3/4 x 3/4 = 9/16.
- green is 1/4 or dented is 1/4, (because they are recessive traits as   we saw in monohybrid cross),
- both green and dented is 1/4 x 1/4 = 1/16.
For a combination of dominant and recessive phenotypes (also called recombinant phenotypes),
- yellow and dented is 3/4 x 1/4 = 3/16 and
- green and round is 1/4 x 3/4 = 3/16.

The overall ratio of different phenotypes such as yellow and round: yellow and dented: green and round: green and dented is 9:3:3:1.

This type of segregation proved that alleles can segregate independent of each other and recombine to make new phenotypes.

II.   NON-MENDELIAN PATTERNS OF INHERITANCE

1. Intermediate inheritance or incomplete dominance: The homozygotes have particular phenotype and the heterozygotes have an intermediate phenotype showing that no single gene is completely dominant. E.g. Snapdragon flowers with red (RR) and white (rr) color flowers are crossed the F1 generation will have all pink flowers (Rr) showing intermediate inheritance. When the F1 is selfed the F2 generation will have a mixture of red (RR), pink (Rr) and white (rr) flowers in a ratio of 1:2:1.

2. Codominance: Both the phenotypes are expressed at about equal level by the expression of two types of proteins by two alleles. E.g. The blood type AB will express both the proteins for the types A and B in the red blood cells. The white clover leaf has two different patterns which are present in different homozygous conditions. Both the patterns will appear in the heterozygous condition.

3. Pleiotropy: One gene or allele codes for more than one phenotype. E.g. albino individuals lack pigments in skin, eye and hair showing the effect of a single mutation in one locus causing varied effects. In severe diseases such as sickle cell anemia or cystic fibrosis several symptoms can be traced to one or few genes. This may be due to the nature of an individual gene affecting many phenotypes or there are several genes in that locus responsible for the varied effects.

4. Epistasis: One gene interferes with the expression of another gene. Several pairs of alleles may interact to affect a single phenotype. Several enzymes interact in a common biosynthetic pathway. If one enzyme is defective, it affects others no matter what allele is present. E.g. skin color in mice is affected by two pairs of alleles and if one locus (pair of alleles) is homozygous recessive, mice are always albino irrespective of the other locus.

5. Multiple genes: Some genes exist in more than two forms. E.g. skin color in humans is determined by three genes (A, B, C). The dominant alleles of the genes result in dark skin and recessive genes in light skin. Based on the combination of the three allele pairs, the skin color varies from light (aa,bb,cc) to dark color (AA,BB,CC). Many complex traits such as height, intelligence or weight are determined by multiple genes (polygenic traits).

6. Sex linked inheritance: The phenotypes affected by genes located on sex chromosomes are expressed depending on the sex of the individuals. The XX - female and XY - male system is followed in humans and many animals. However, there are other systems such as ZW -female and ZZ - male in birds. The genes present on only one sex chromosome - for example, X in male (XY) is referred to as hemizygous condition. There are several sex linked traits such as baldness, hemophilia and muscular dystrophy.

7. Maternal inheritance: The genes present in mitochondria and chloroplasts are always inherited maternally. Only the nuclear genes are carried on from one gamete to another by the male and the mitochondria and chloroplasts present in the egg are copied in the zygote (after fertilization) and passed on to next generation. E.g. coloration of stem in four-o'clock plant is due to the chlorophyll content determined by chloroplast genes derived from female parent.

8. Environmental effect on gene expression: The interaction of environment on gene expression results in wider variation especially in traits controlled by multiple genes. E.g. skin color determined by three alleles is affected further by sunlight intensifying the melanin pigmentation. Other examples of environment on gene expression include nutrition and exercise on weight or height. The flowers of hydrangea may be blue if grown on acidic soil or pink if grown in alkaline soil.

III. MENDELIAN INHERITANCE OF HUMAN GENETIC DISORDERS

There are several genetic disorders that are inherited based on same principles as Mendel proposed. Since we cannot do breeding experiments with humans, we use pedigree analysis to study the inheritance pattern of a particular character and asses if they are dominantly or recessively inherited. For example, if a trait is recessive, it will be expressed only if the person showing the phenotype is homozygous. If such a homozygous recessive individual marries someone without that trait (unknown genotype), we can tell if the other person is homozygous dominant or heterozygous based on the segregation of traits in their children. If all of them do not have that trait the other person is a homozygous dominant or is some children show the trait, that person is heterozygous as illustrated below.

Parent 1 Homozygous recessive and shows the phenotype (aa) and Parent 2 with unknown genotype and normal phenotype(??)

If all children are normal without the recessive phenotype – Parent 2 is AA.If some children show the phenotype as Parent 1, then the parent 2 has heterozygous genotype (Aa).

On the other hand, if a trait is dominant, the parents will show the trait and also will pass on to all the first generation if they are homozygous and to some of the children if they are heterozygous, assuming the other parent is homozygous recessive (no trait). Pedigree analysis is illustrated in the following example of a recessively inherited trait (cystic fibrosis). Let us denote the alleles as CC or cc.

If the parent is →	Homozygous dominant	Heterozygous	Homozygous recessive
Genotype	CC	Cc	cc
Phenotype	No disease	No disease but a carrier	Disease
Children (F1)	All children will be normal, irrespective of other parent.	Some children will be diseased, if the other parent is cc or even Cc.	If other parent is homozygous dominant, no children will show disease. Other cases (Cc and cc), some will show disease.

Inheritance of selected traits in humans

Selected examples of recessively and dominantly inherited disorders in humans are briefly discussed below. The occurrence of a particular trait in human population varies based on their effect in the survival and reproduction. If a trait is homozygous and lethal as in the case of cystic fibrosis (recessive) or hypercholesterolemia (dominant), the individual will not leave until reproductive stage to pass on that trait. However, if the individual is heterozygous and the disease is not that severe, they will serve as a carrier and pass on the genes or trait to next generation. In general, the recessive alleles could be the predominant ones whether the trait has deleterious effect or no effect on survival.

There are several traits that are determined by multiple genes. Such polygenic traits show wide variations in the phenotype and are relatively complex to analyze by simple mendelian inheritance. Examples of polygenic traits include heart disease, cancer, diabetes, schizophrenia, manic depression, and alcoholism. In addition to these, other traits such as height, weight, skin color and general behaviors are regulated by multiple genes. Also, the environmental and social conditions will have significant influence on the expression of these phenotypes.

Major Concepts
1. Genetic material DNA stores information and it can be replicated.
2. The structure of genetic material was elucidated as double helix with ribose –phosphate backbone and nitrogenous bases making H-bonds
3. Replication of DNA is semiconservative and it involves several proteins.
4. Repairing the mistakes in DNA replication or any damages caused by other factors is critical to prevent any mutations.

Outline:
I.   Search for the genetic material.
II. DNA structure.
III. DNA replication.
IV. DNA repair.

I.   SEARCH FOR THE GENETIC MATERIAL

Proteins were initially considered to be the genetic material due to the diversity of their composition (20 amino acids) and function. Presence of proteins in chromosomes further strengthened this notion. Nucleic acids were considered to be too simple (only four bases) to carry on the hereditary function. However, the following experiments proved that DNA is the material that stores genetic information and passes it on from generation to generation.

A. Evidence of DNA transforming bacteria.
In **1928, Fredrick Griffith** studied different strains *of Streptococcus pneumoniae* (bacteria causing pneumonia in humans). They used an S-strain (smooth; has a smooth polysaccharide coating) which can cause disease in mice and an R-strain (rough; no polysaccharide) which did not cause the disease when injected in mice. He heat killed the S-strain which also did not cause any disease. However, a mixture of heat killed S-strain and R-strain caused disease and killed the mice when injected together. He concluded that the heat killed S-strain transformed the R-strain by transferring the "genetic principle".

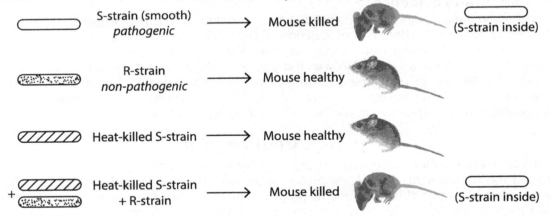

Even though one can argue that proteins are denatured during heating and only DNA can renature and transform, this did not conclusively prove that it was DNA and not protein that transformed the R-strain.

B. In **1944, Oswald Avery, Colin McLeod and Maclyn McCarty** isolated pure DNA from S-strain, mixed with R-strain to transform the later into a disease causing strain. This was the first in vitro transformation of one bacterial strain by introducing DNA from another bacterial strain. This was a major milestone in molecular biology that demonstrated the DNA as genetic material and that genetic transformation with DNA is possible. This was not taken seriously until further evidence came from an independent experiment.

C. Evidence of viral DNA programming bacteria

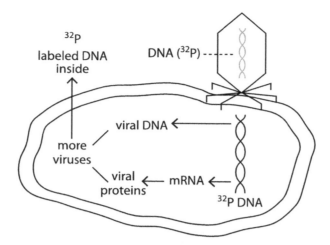

Bacteriophages are viruses infecting bacteria. Viruses contain DNA or RNA genome with a protein capsid (envelope). In **1952**, **Alfred Hershey** and **Martha Chase** used a T2 bacteriophage which was known to inject part of its contents into bacteria to program the cells to make more viruses. Hershey and Chase wanted to find out if the genetic material that is injected into bacteria was DNA or protein. So they cultured two batches of the T2 phage separately in media containing ^{35}S and ^{32}P to label proteins and DNA respectively. Then they isolated the phages and used them to infect bacteria cultured without any radioisotope. After infection, they mixed the contents vigorously in a kitchen blender to shake off the phages from the bacteria. The mixture was then centrifuged to pellet the bacteria and retain the phages in supernatant. The pellet fraction (bacteria) contained most of the ^{32}P and the supernatant contained most of the ^{35}S, indicating that DNA was the genetic material injected into bacterial cells to program the cells to make more viruses.

D. Other supporting evidence

In addition to above results, other circumstantial evidence including **Erwin Chargaff**'s report in **1950** that different species contained different compositions of DNA (GC-content) and the chromosomes going through duplication during cell division supported that DNA is the genetic material carrying hereditary information. Once it was known that DNA was the genetic material, scientists were rushing to elucidate the structure of DNA and to understand its replicatio   ss. Chargaff had also reported that the amounts of adenine and thymine were approximately   OR   nd the amounts of guanine and cytosine were approximately equal. These were useful in elucidating the structure of DNA.

II. DNA STRUCTURE

The nucleotide bases and their covalent bonds in a polymer were known in 1950 but the three-dimensional structure and the mechanism of DNA replication were not known. **Linus Pauling** in California had developed models of protein structures and he proposed that DNA is a triple helix. **Maurice Wilkins** and **Rosalind Franklin** in King's College London were studying the X-ray crystallography structure of DNA. **James Watson** from America and **Francis Crick** of England were working on the chemistry of DNA in Cambridge University, London using chemical models of the bases to develop a three-dimensional structure.

During this investigation Watson, visited and saw the X-ray crystallography picture of DNA taken by Rosalind Franklin. Those pictures containing spots and smudges due to X-ray diffraction through cross sections of a DNA strand gave insight into the possible structure of DNA. Two major pieces of information obtained from the pictures were that the diameter of DNA was 2 nm and the bases were stacked perpendicular to the strand with a distance of 0.34 nm between the bases. Later, Watson and Crick used the chemical models and constructed the double helix structure of DNA by trying different possible combinations. The results from the findings of Watson & Crick, Maurice Wilkins and Rosalind Franklin were published in **1953** in Nature. The main features of DNA double helix are summarized below.

1. DNA consists of two strands that are H-bonded together with a width of 2 nm.
2. The two strands turn right to make a right-handed helix (turns clockwise, when looked through cross section). The strands are like the ropes of a ladder with the bases making the rungs.
3. The hydrophilic sugar-phosphate is on the outside of helix. The negatively charged P-groups make DNA soluble in aqueous solution.
4. The hydrophobic nitrogenous bases are stacked inside in a perpendicular manner to the strand. The distance between two base pairs is 0.34 nm. There are 10 base pairs per turn.
5. Adenine pairs with thymine with 2 H-bonds and guanine pairs with cytosine with 3 H-bonds. This satisfies the Chargaff's finding that the contents of A=T and G=C. This is referred to as complementary base pairing
6. The two strands run in opposite direction i.e anti parallel orientation. The starting of DNA has a phosphate group attached to the 5th C of ribose (5') and the other end has a -OH group attached to the 3rd C of ribose (3').
7. The helical turns make a major groove and a minor groove between the adjacent turns.
8. From this structure it was evident that DNA stores information in its sequence of bases (4 bases with infinite possibilities of various sequence and lengths).
9. Based on the complementary base pairing, the DNA replication was proposed to be semiconservative (explained later). New copy is made from a template DNA with high specificity.

Later in 1962, Watson, Crick and Wilkins were awarded a Nobel Prize for elucidating the 3-dimensional structure of DNA. Rosalind Franklin had passed away before this time and the Nobel Prize is not awarded posthumously.

Supercoiling
Double helix of the DNA coils onto itself resulting in supercoiled DNA. This occurs in circular DNA (plasmids, bacterial chromosome, chloroplast and mitochondrial DNA) and linear eukaryotic chromosomes. Supercoiling is important to keep the DNA compact in the cell and during DNA replication. The DNA strands could be linear or circular. The circular DNA can be open circular or supercoiled.

DNA is present mostly in double stranded form. However single stranded DNA is present in viral genomes. The double stranded nature of DNA is important for its stability and proof-reading during replication. The major helical forms of DNA and their features are listed in the following table.

Denaturing/renaturing DNA
Since the double helix of DNA is bonded with H-bonds they can be separated by heating or exposing to

alkaline condition. The same DNA can be renatured to its original form (called hybridization, they rejoin due to complementary base pairing) by gradual cooling or neutralizing the alkaline solution with a mild acid. This mechanism is extensively used to study DNA.

III. DNA REPLICATION

A. DNA replication is semiconservative

Semiconservative refers to the fact that half of a newly made DNA is the old template. In other words, one strand is used as a template to make new strand based on complementary base pairing rules (A:T and G:C). First *in vitro* DNA synthesis was performed by Arthur Kornberg in 1953 using a template DNA, DNA polymerase and four nucleotides. If any one of the nucleotides was missing DNA synthesis will stop. This was done in a test tube without any cells demonstrating that DNA can replicate itself.

However, the semiconservative mechanism (shown above) was proven by an experiment by **Matthew Meselson** and **Franklin Stahl** in **1957**. They used ^{14}N (lighter) and ^{15}N heavier) isotopes to distinguish the old DNA template and new DNA made from the template. First they grew bacteria in a medium containing ^{15}N (in ammonium chloride) for 17 generations which resulted in the nitrogenous bases in DNA labeled with ^{15}N. They collected bacterial sample from this culture (sample 1) and then inoculated into a medium containing ^{14}N. They allowed it to replicate once (20 minutes) and collected the second sample after one DNA replication (sample 2). The bacteria were allowed to replicate once more (40 minutes) to undergo another DNA replication. The third sample was collected after 60 minutes (sample 3). They isolated DNA from these samples using cesium chloride density gradient centrifugation which can separate according to the density of each DNA (heavier the DNA the lower will be that DNA band in the centrifuge tube). The following results were obtained.

These results indicated that the new DNA strand synthesized in sample 2 after one DNA replication/cell division is a combination of old (^{15}N-DNA) and new (^{14}N-DNA) DNA strands. If both strands were new, one would expect two bands of ^{15}N and ^{14}N DNA strands. This proved that DNA replicates by semiconservative mode, i.e. half old template and half newly made DNA.

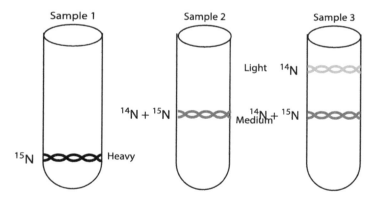

B. Mechanism of DNA replication

DNA replication starts in places called *origin of replication* which is a location on DNA molecule with a specific sequence that is recognized by enzymes involved in DNA replication. As we saw earlier, bacterial chromosomes and plasmids contain a single origin of replication whereas eukaryotic chromosomes contain multiple origins of replication. Bacterial origin of replication is about 245 bp long. In eukaryotes, the origin of replication is not that well defined.

DNA replication in the cell is complex and requires concerted action of several proteins as mentioned above. Under *in vitro* condition, DNA template, DNA primer (short oligonucleotide), Mg^{++}, DNA polymerase, dNTPs in a suitable buffer (to maintain optimum salt, pH condition) will be enough to synthesize DNA.

DNA Replication *in vivo*

The diagram in the next page gives an overview of DNA replication. Please note that the picture is not to scale in terms of relative dimensions of different sub-diagrams. The RNA primers shown are longer than what is shown here and the enzymes are much bigger than the DNA strand itself. DNA replication starts at the origin of replication and proceeds bidirectionally. The replication bubble consists of two replication forks joined together which actually expand wider as the DNA replication progresses.

Initiation:

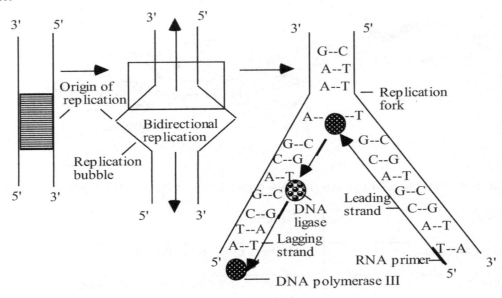

- It starts with relaxation of supercoiling at the origin(s) of replication (ORI) by topoisomerase. There is a single origin of replication in prokaryotic DNA and multiple origins in eukaryotic DNA.
- The relaxed DNA helix is opened to make a replication fork and the resulting single stranded DNA is stabilized by SSB proteins.
- Primase makes a RNA primer (which provides a free 3'-OH group, and a primer is needed for the DNA polymerase to work) to start the new DNA synthesis.

Elongation

* DNA polymerase III (a complex protein) binds to the DNA template + RNA-primer region and starts to add nucleotides that are complementary to the template strand as shown below. It adds at a rate of about 1000 nucleotides/sec in prokaryotes.
* The DNA synthesis always happens 5' to 3'. This is due to the nature of the enzyme DNA polymerase to link new deoxy-nucleoside triphosphates (dNTPs) only to the 3'-OH group. A <u>leading strand</u> is synthesized continuously from 5' to 3' based on the template.
* Since the opposite strand is not fully open to continue DNA synthesis from 5' to 3' direction, DNA is synthesized in small fragments which are called <u>Okazaki fragments</u>. This strand is called the <u>lagging strand</u> (made slowly after the leading strand). The Okazaki fragments are approximately 100-200 bases in eukaryotes and 1000-2000 bases in prokaryotes.
* Once the new DNA strand is synthesized, DNA polymerase III proofreads it and makes sure the errors are removed. DNA polymerase I removes the RNA primer and completes DNA strand.
* Once the small fragments are completed, DNA ligase joins the two ends of DNA strands to complete DNA replication. DNA gyrase facilitates supercoiling of DNA to compact the chromosomes into nucleosomes.

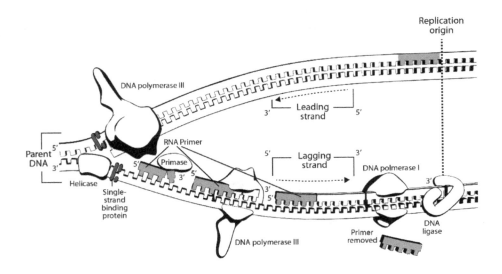

The proteins that play a major role in DNA replication are listed in the following Table.

	Protein	Function
1.	Topoisomerase	Relaxes the supercoiled DNA.
2.	Helicase	Unwinds the double helix into single stranded DNA.
3.	SSB	Single stranded DNA binding protein. Stabilizes the ssDNA.
4.	Primase	Synthesizes RNA primers.
5.	DNA polymerase I	Erases RNA primers and fills in the gaps.
6.	DNA polymerase III Holoenzyme.	DNA synthesis, proof reading, exonuclease activity and repair.
7.	DNA ligase	Covalently joins free 3' and 5' ends of two DNA fragments through phosphodiester linkage.
8.	DNA gyrase	Introduces supercoiling in DNA.

DNA Replication Complex: This diagram provides a good summary of the DNA replication complex once it started at the origin of replication. Pay attention to the various proteins and the new leading and lagging strands of DNA being made. PCNA stand for Proliferating Cell Nuclear Antigen that is needed as a cofactor for the DNA Polymerase III.

DNA ELONGATION COMPLEX

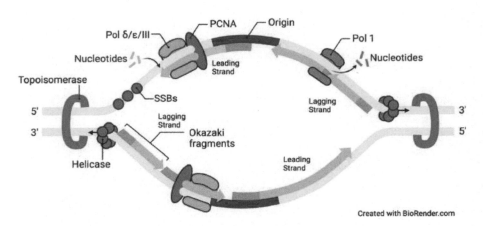

Created with BioRender.com

IV.   DNA REPAIR

It is very important for the cells to correct any errors in DNA replication or any damage caused to the DNA after the replication because such errors may be fatal sometimes. Hence, the mistakes in DNA replication and the mutations caused by carcinogenic chemicals, X-rays etc. must be repaired before the DNA can function and replicate again. If left uncorrected, it results in stable mutations that will be passed on to next generation of cells or organisms. There are two major types of DNA repair mechanisms operating in the cell.

1. **Mismatch repair** is done to correct the errors made during DNA replication. DNA polymerase III makes approximately 1 in 10,000 mistakes before correcting the errors. Then, it proofreads the newly made DNA, removes the wrong bases and remake the DNA to minimize the errors to 1 in a billion. These error corrections use the mismatch repair mechanism by checking the complementary base pairing. E.g. problem in mismatch repair causes colon cancer.

2. **Excision repair** occurs after a cell divides and is in the G1 phase or G2 phase. This damage is caused by carcinogens and mutagenic radiations altering the bases or making pyrimidine dimers (e.g.T-T). Such mutations are constantly monitored by over 50 different enzymes and corrected by excising the damaged strand of DNA (by an endonuclease) and making a new matching strand (by DNA polymerase and DNA ligase) in its place. E.g. the disease xeroderma pigmentosum is caused by lack of enzyme(s) involved in excision repair.

3. **Telomere Repair:** The enzyme telomerase extends the 3' end of the telomere region and allows the RNA primer to bind to the extended region and thus protect the telomere from being degraded. This occurs in young and actively growing cells as well as cancer cells making them almost immortal.

Concepts

1) A gene is a linear segment of DNA that contains the information needed to synthesize or 'express' a particular gene product (RNA or protein).
2) Protein expression involves two sequential steps: (1) transcription of mRNA from DNA and (2) translation of mRNA to produce a polypeptide chain.
3) Transcription relies on complementary base-pairing to copy the nucleotide sequence information present in one strand of the double helix.
4) Messenger RNAs are processed prior to translation. In eukaryotes, this includes the removal or splicing of introns.
5) Translation takes place in the ribosome, and relies upon a highly conserved genetic code.
6) Some newly synthesized polypeptides must undergo additional chemical modifications before they become mature, functional proteins.
7) Mutations are changes in the genetic information encoded in DNA and may change the sequence of amino acids in the protein formed from the mutated gene.

Outline

I. Transcription: RNA synthesis
II. RNA processing.
III. Genetic Language and Mutations
IV. Translation: Protein synthesis
V. Protein processing.

I. TRANSCRIPTION

The central dogma of molecular biology originally proposed by Francis Crick states that DNA codes for RNA codes for protein. This is a well-established fact and not a dogma anymore.

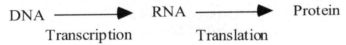

DNA ⟶ RNA ⟶ Protein
    Transcription   Translation

The differences between DNA and RNA are summarized in the Figure below.

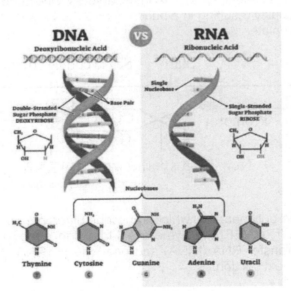

We will look at RNA synthesis next and see how it is processed before translation.

A. Transcription process:

RNA is synthesized in 5' to 3' direction by RNA polymerase from a DNA template in the presence of nucleoside triphosphates (NTPs), Mg^{++} at suitable pH and salt condition. RNA polymerases do not need a primer due to the nature of their active site. Knowing the structure of a gene and the factors involved in transcription are important in understanding the transcription process.

The RNA polymerase acts in concert with several other proteins which bind to DNA and affect transcription which are called **trans-acting factors** or simply **transcription factors**. The transcription factors recognize specific sequences on the DNA called **cis-acting elements**. These elements include, but are not limited to the promoter and/or an enhancer or suppressor element. These are specific regions on the DNA which affect the amount, rate and accuracy of transcription. The promoter in eukaryotes consists of a TATA box (TATAA rich region -10 bp), GC box (-35-40 bp) and CAAT box (-90-110 bp) on the sense/coding strand. It affects the accuracy and amount of transcription. The enhancer or suppressers are called regulatory regions which when bound by transcription factors result in more active or less active transcription respectively. Once the RNA polymerase + transcription factors bind to promoter, they open the double helix and start to transcribe RNA by incorporating NTPs (C U A G) complementary to the template DNA strand (G A T C). The opposite strand is not transcribed.

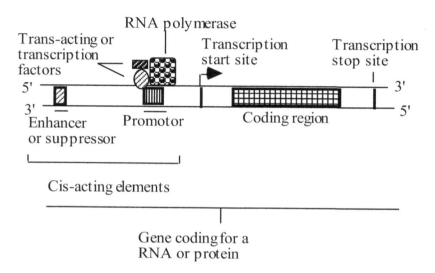

Transcription proceeds at approximately 60 nucleotides per sec and stops at the transcription stop site. The stop site is denoted by the sequence AATAAA in eukaryotes. One gene can be transcribed by several RNA polymerases simultaneously resulting in a bunch of mRNAs varying from longest to shortest mRNA generated from one DNA template.

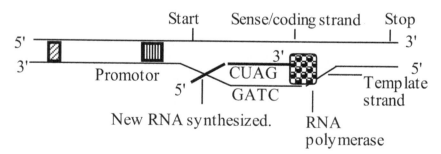

There are three types of RNA polymerases, which transcribe different RNA molecules. RNA polymerase I transcribes ribosomal RNA (rRNA), RNA polymerase II transcribes messenger RNA (mRNA) and RNA polymerase III transcribes transfer RNA (tRNA) and one type of rRNA. The differences among these RNAs are explained later in next section.

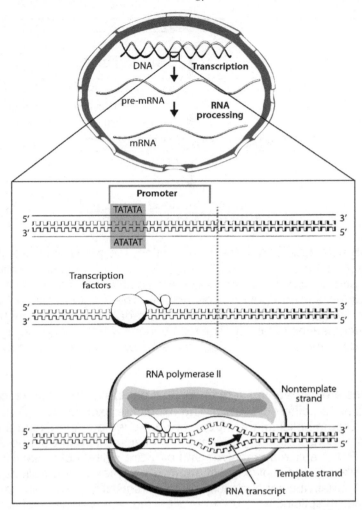

Differences between prokaryotes and eukaryotes:

In prokaryotes, many genes are situated continuously in one operon (set of genes with one control element i.e. promoter/operator). One transcription event results in a single transcript (mRNA) that codes for more than one protein. This is called polycistronic i.e. many messages per transcription. Also, prokaryotes transcribe and translate simultaneously because there is no nuclear membrane to separate transcription and translation. Prokaryotes have only one type of RNA polymerase. Moreover, prokaryotic RNA does not go through any processing such as polyadenylation or intron (intervening sequences) removal before translation.

Eukaryotic transcription is in the nucleus, physically separate from the cytoplasm, where translation takes place. Also, eukaryotic genes are monocistronic i.e. one gene transcribed per transcription, each transcript coding for one protein. Some viruses in eukaryotic cells have been shown to have polycistronic messages. In addition, eukaryotic RNAs contain intervening sequences called introns which are removed during RNA processing explained below. Eukaryotic RNA also goes through attachment of poly A + RNA and Guanine-cap.

II. <u>RNA PROCESSING IN EUKARYOTES</u>

Eukaryotic RNA undergoes extensive processing inside nucleus before it leaves for translation in cytoplasm. The two major types of processing are given below.

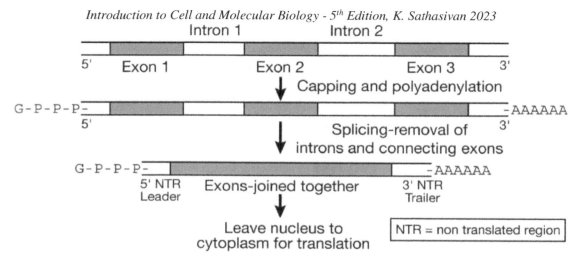

1. Capping and polyadenylation*: After transcription, the phosphate group of a modified form of guanosine triphosphate (GTP) is added to the 5' end of RNA. This process is called capping and it helps in protecting the mRNA and to mark the 5' end as starting point for translation. At 3' end a stretch of polyAs (adenines) are added by an enzyme poly(A) polymerase. The length of polyA tail varies from 30 - 200 Adenines. Poly(A) tail protects the mRNA from being degraded. However, only the mRNAs are capped and polyadenylated to increase their stability. The rRNA and tRNA do not go through such polyadenylation and g-capping but they do some times go through the splicing process. Such polyA+ RNA is not found in prokaryotes.

2. Splicing: The introns are intervening sequences that generally do not code for a protein. Very rarely, introns may code for a smaller, different protein. The exons are expressed regions coding for a protein or a segment of a protein. During splicing, the introns are removed and the exons are joined together. NTR refers to non-translated regions which are present in processed RNA at 5' and 3' ends but they do not code for protein. Some RNAs splice themselves and they are called autocatalytic RNAs. This process is called self-splicing. In other RNAs, splicing occurs in a complex called *splicesome* made up of small nuclear RNAs (snRNAs), small nuclear ribonucleoproteins (snRNPs-called "snurps") and proteins. Almost all eukaryotic RNAs undergo splicing and further processing. A few genes lack introns and they undergo different processing.

III. THE GENETIC LANGUAGE AND MUTATIONS

Initially, the relationship between DNA, RNA and proteins was not clearly understood. In **1909**, an English Physician **Archibald Garrod** studied the disease alkaptonuria in which the chemical alkapton accumulates in the urine and it makes the urine turn black upon exposure to air. Garrod suggested that such errors of metabolism are due to lack of specific enzymes involved in the pathway and such errors can be inherited genetically. However, this was not considered seriously until further evidence on genes and enzymes was obtained.

A. One gene-one polypeptide hypothesis:
Biochemists accumulated evidence that many metabolic reactions are performed by enzymes in 1900s. In the 1940s **George Beadle and Edward Tatum** were studying mutants of a fungus *Neurospora crassa.* The normal *Neurospora,* grown on a minimal medium containing defined minerals and no other nutritional supplements, are called wild type or prototrophs. Beadle and Tatum generated mutants of *Neurospora* that can not grow on minimal medium without additional supplements such as amino acids or sugars by treating the fungus with X-rays. Such nutritional mutants are called auxotrophs (increased nourishment/feeding).

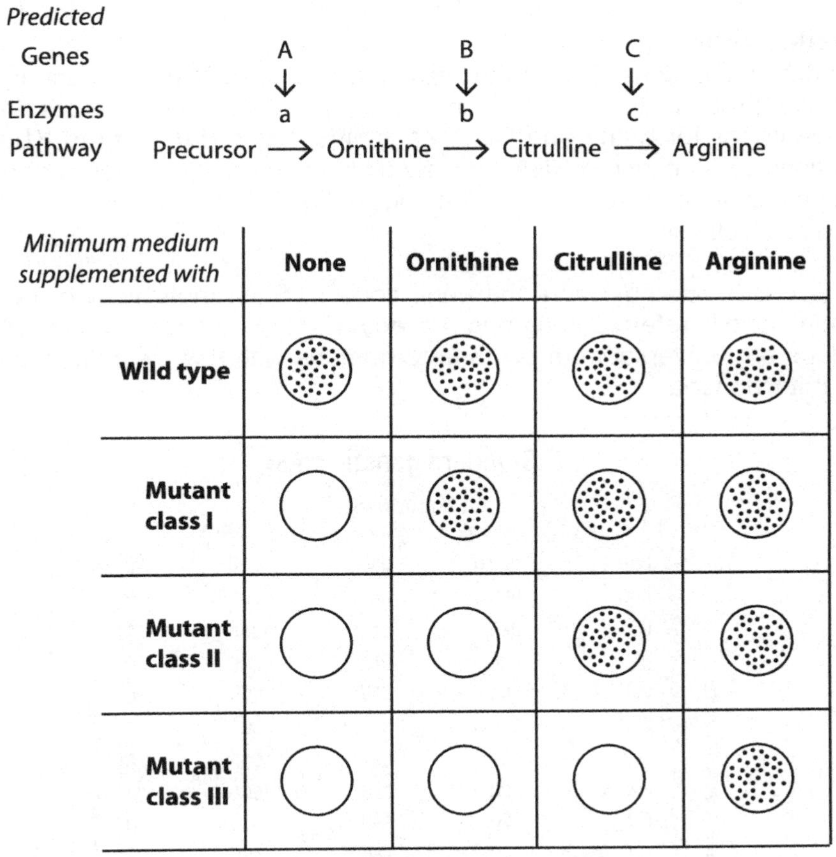

Predicted

Genes	A	B	C
	↓	↓	↓
Enzymes	a	b	c
Pathway	Precursor → Ornithine →	Citrulline →	Arginine

Minimum medium supplemented with	None	Ornithine	Citrulline	Arginine
Wild type	●	●	●	●
Mutant class I	○	●	●	●
Mutant class II	○	○	●	●
Mutant class III	○	○	○	●

In one study, (as shown in the Figure above) the mutants were selected by plating them on minimal media alone and with supplements in the biosynthesis of arginine. Filled circle means fungus is growing. The pathway of making arginine was fairly well known except for the enzymes; Precursor → Ornithine → Citrulline → Arginine. So, if a mutant survives on media with a specific intermediate of this pathway, say citrulline, (and not with ornithine) it means that mutant can continue the pathway beyond citrulline and there is a mutation in the enzyme making citrulline. Based on these results, Beadle and Tatum concluded that one enzyme is coded by one gene and any mutation in that gene will result in a mutant enzyme. This one gene-one enzyme hypothesis was later modified to one gene-one polypepetide hypothesis.

B. The genetic language
The flow of genetic information proposed by Crick was resolved by the results of several experiments.

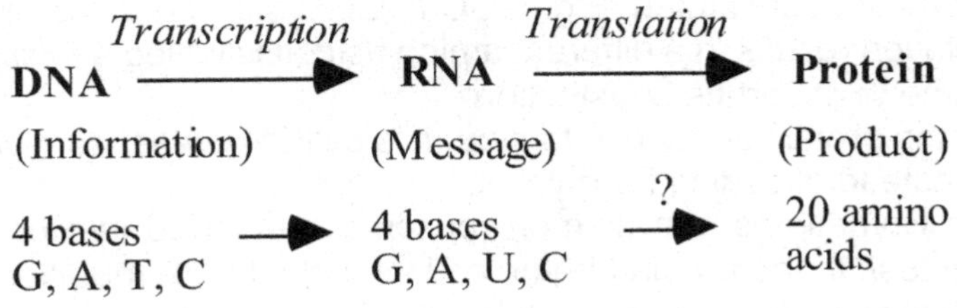

DNA —*Transcription*→ RNA —*Translation*→ Protein
(Information) (Message) (Product)
4 bases G, A, T, C → 4 bases G, A, U, C —?→ 20 amino acids

The first question was to understand how information is communicated from DNA to protein. The messenger hypothesis by **Crick**, **Sydney Brenner** and **Francois Jacob** proposed that DNA is first copied (transcribed) into a messenger RNA (mRNA), which is translated into protein using adapters (transfer RNA; tRNA). The possibility of a coding system (using codons) was obvious because DNA and RNA have only 4 bases and protein has 20 amino acids. This was resolved by simple logic as follows:

If one base codes for one amino acid, it can code for only 4 amino acids, if two bases code for one amino acid, only $4^2 = 16$ amino acids are possible, if three bases code for one amino acid, $4^3 = 64$ amino acids are possible, which will account for the 20 amino acids seen in the codon table below.

135

B. Universal genetic code

To resolve all the different codons, **Marshall Nirenberg** and **J. H. Matthei** made synthetic mRNAs and used them to make proteins in vitro. In 1961, they published their results that UUU codes for phenylalanine, AAA codes for lysine and CCC for proline. Later **Har Gobind Khorana** made various possible combinations of synthetic mRNA and decoded many of the other codons. Also, there were codons for starting a polypeptide and stopping the polypeptide called start codons (AUG) and stop codons (UGA, UAG, UAA) respectively.

Some amino acids were coded by more than one codons. Such multiplicity or redundancy of codons coding for one amino acid is referred to as **degeneracy**. E.g.. glycine is coded by GGG, GGA, GGU and GGC. These codons are universal from bacteria to humans with few exceptions such as paramecium, tetrahymena and mitochondria.

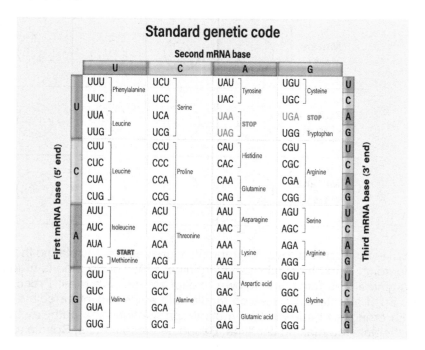

D. Mutations:

Mutations occurring in and around genes may affect protein synthesis, sequence and function. The different types of mutations and their effects on proteins are listed below.

a. Point mutations.

Single base pair is changed or substituted with another. Sometimes it has no effect on protein sequence or function if similar codons are substituted. E.g. GGC to GGG still codes for Glycine.

However, if the point mutation results in a different amino acid, it is called a *missense mutation*. E.g. GGC to GAC will result in glycine to aspartate substitution.

If the change resulted in the protein sequence to stop, it is called *non-sense mutation*. E.g.. GGA to UGA will result in stop signal instead of coding for glycine.

b. Insertions or deletions: Sometimes one or more bases are inserted into or deleted from the coding sequence resulting in *frameshift* (the reading frame codons get altered) mutations. E.g. GGC, GGA, GGC codes for glycine-glycine-glycine. If one base is deleted in this sequence, say the third base C is deleted, the reading frame now shifts to GGG, GAG and GC- making a protein with gly-glutamate-alanine. Similar frame shifts can happen if one or more bases are inserted. These are the mutations with worst possible effects on the protein sequence and function. These insertions, deletions can also happen at chromosomal level covering a large region.

c. Inversion and translocation: Sometimes, two segments of a chromosome are inverted or translocated. Inversion results in flipping the order of genes such as A-B-C becomes C-B-A whereas translocations involve moving a part of chromosome from one place to another or to a different chromosome.

Mutations are important mechanisms to create new genes with novel functions but may also result in less effective or non-functioning proteins with severe consequences.

Mutagenesis: Mutations may be caused by the following mechanisms.
a. Natural: spontaneous mutations due to errors in DNA replication, repair and recombination. Some viruses can also cause mutations by interrupting the reading frame of an important gene.
b. Chemical mutagens: These may be base analogs (e.g. 5-bromo uracil), reactive chemicals (e.g. nitroso compounds) or intercalating chemicals (ethidium bromide).
c. physical mutagens: X-rays, UV rays can also result in mutations. Both short wave and long wave UV light (present in sunlight and tanning salon lights).

IV.   PROTEIN SYNTHESIS

Protein synthesis occurs in the cytoplasm in eukaryotic cells. Before looking at the details of translation, let us review the different RNA molecules in translation and their functions. Almost all cellular RNA is single stranded and forms unique secondary structures based on sequence.

A. RNA types and functions:
1. Transfer RNA (tRNA) is a small (~75-80 bases long) RNA folded into a clover leaf shape. It functions as an adapter between mRNA and ribosomes during protein synthesis. There are 45 different types of tRNAs specific for various amino acids. The amino acids are activated and then attached at the 3' region of tRNA. Each tRNA has an anticodon that is complementary to the codon in mRNA. Since there are 64 codons and only 45 tRNAs, the third base in tRNA is sometimes inosine which can recognize A, U or C on mRNA. Inosine is a modified form of Guanine and it does not base pair with G. This flexibility of the third base to bond with more than one codon is called wobble.

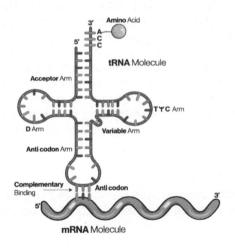

Codon Anti codon binding

2. **Ribosomal RNA (rRNA)** is a major component of ribosomes. Approximately 60% of ribosomes are made up of rRNA and 40% are ribosomal proteins. rRNA is the most abundant form of RNA in cells. Ribosomes are made up of small and large subunits and they coordinate the protein synthesis by coupling the mRNA and tRNAs carrying various amino acids. Also, they perform the peptidyl transferase activity i.e. making peptide bonds between amino acids to make proteins. The small and large subunits assemble just before they begin protein synthesis. Ribosomes have two specific sites to bind tRNAs and perform peptide bonding. The P-site holds the tRNA carrying the growing polypeptide chain (peptidyl tRNA) and the A-site holds the tRNA carrying the next amino acid to be added (aminoacyl tRNA). The E-site (exit) is where the tRNAs leave the ribosome.

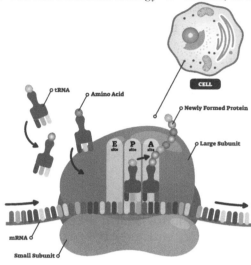

3. Messenger RNA (mRNA) carries the message from the gene to be translated into protein. As we saw earlier, the mRNA alone has poly(A) tail and travels to cytoplasm to be translated. mRNAs vary in length from 100 bases to 15 kilobases. The processed mRNA carry regions that are recognized by the ribosomes to start protein synthesis. In prokaryotes, the ribosome recognition site is called the Shine-Dalgarno region. In eukaryotes, the ribosome recognition site is not that well defined. However, the translation in all organisms starts with an AUG codon.

B. Activation of amino acids and attachment to tRNAs.
Selection of a specific amino acid and attaching to the corresponding tRNA that has the proper anticodon is very important for specificity. Since the peptide bonds are thermodynamically unfavorable, the amino acids must be activated and attached to the 3'-OH group of tRNA for easy transfer to the elongating polypeptide. This activation and attachment are done by aminoacyl-tRNA synthetases. There is at least one enzyme for each amino acid and its appropriate tRNA.
1. It binds to the right amino acid at its -COOH terminus and attaches an AMP by hydrolyzing an ATP.
2. The enzyme recognizes the tRNA by its secondary structure and anticodon.
3. Then it transfers the amino acid to the 3-OH group of the correct tRNA and AMP is detached. Then it releases the aminoacyl tRNA.

C. Protein synthesis:
This process can be explained in three stages namely initiation, elongation and termination. The structure of ribosomes and three RNAs involved have been explained earlier.

1. Initiation:
The small subunit of ribosome first recognizes the ribosome binding site (Shine-Dalgarno region in prokaryotes; the G-cap and a consensus region near the start codons in eukaryotic mRNA) at the 5' NTR. The first codon is almost always methionine. A special tRNA carrying a modified methionine (formyl Met) binds to the P-site. In addition, 3 initiation factors (IF; proteins that help in starting translation) and GTP bind to form initiation complex. The large subunit comes in and joins with the small subunit and rest of the initiation complex. The GTP is hydrolyzed in this step.

2. Elongation:

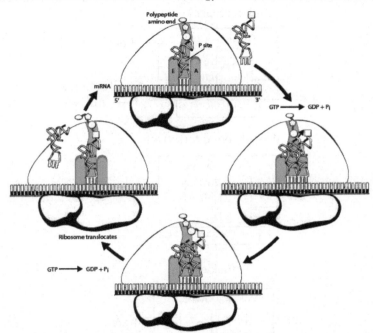

The elongation of polypeptide happens in three steps. This elongation process is shown below in a conceptual manner followed by a more detailed diagram.

a. Codon recognition: An elongation factor (EF; proteins that help in extension of polypeptide chain) brings an appropriate aminoacyl tRNA (tRNA for next codon + corresponding amino acid) and places it on the A-site. A GTP attached to EF is hydrolyzed for this step.

b. Peptide bond formation: The peptidyl transferase activity of ribosomes transfers the first Methionine (or a growing polypeptide) from P-site tRNA to A-site and makes a peptide bond between the carboxyl terminus of previous amino acid and the amino terminus of incoming amino acid. The tRNA at P-site (empty with no amino acid or protein) moves from the P-site to E- site (exit) and leaves the ribosome.

c. Translocation: The t-RNA at A-site is translocated to P-site. Another GTP is hydrolyzed. The mRNA codons and corresponding tRNA are H-bonded. Hence when the peptidyl tRNA (tRNA with the growing polypeptide) moves from A-site to P-site the mRNA also slides along. As mentioned earlier, the t-RNA that was in the P-site moves to E-site and then leaves the ribosome. Now the next codon comes to A-site. The elongation continues with the next codon recognition again, peptide bond formation and translocation. Each elongation step takes about 60 milliseconds.

Codon recognition

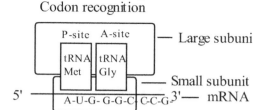

Peptide bond formation

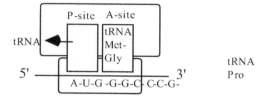

Translocation

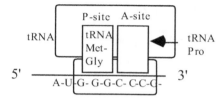

a.

3. Termination.

The polypeptide elongation continues until the codon (termination signal: UAA, UAG or UAG) on mRNA reaches the A-site. A release factor (protein) binds to this stop codon and makes peptidyl transferase add H2O to the growing polypeptide chain. This step releases the completed polypeptide from the tRNA at P-site from the ribosome. The ribosome subunits separate and go on to start another polypeptide synthesis.

One mRNA can be translated simultaneously by several ribosomes making several polypeptides continuously from one template. This combination one mRNA and many ribosomes is called a **polysome.**

stop

and

of

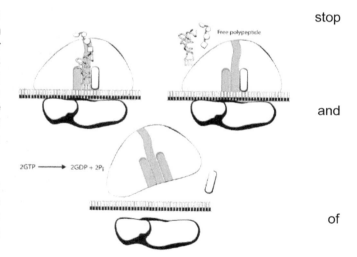

V. PROTEIN PROCESSING

Almost all the proteins made in eukaryotic cells undergo some form of processing before they start functioning. Some examples of protein processing are given below.

1. The amino terminal is sometimes cleaved to activate the protein or to remove a target signal (a segment that tags a protein for a specific destination in a cell or for secretion).
2. Disulfide bonds are formed between two cystines.
3. Some amino acid side chains are chemically modified. E.g. hydroxy proline or glycine.
4. Glycosylation of some residues on the protein.
5. Zymogen activation: An inactive protein such as pre-pro-insulin is processed to remove part of the polypeptide and disulfide bonds are formed to become an active insulin.

Summary:

The DNA double helix has two major functions, namely to replicate and pass on the genetic information to next generation and to be used as template for mRNA synthesis in a highly regulated manner. The mRNA transcribed from DNA is processed in eukaryotes by adding a 5' G-cap and poly (A) tail. In prokaryotes, the mRNA is translated simultaneously. The translation occurs in cytoplasm of eukaryotes where small subunit of ribosome recognizes the 5' mRNA region starts the initiation complex. The large subunit joins and helps in making the polypeptide. The polypeptide is processed before it starts to function.

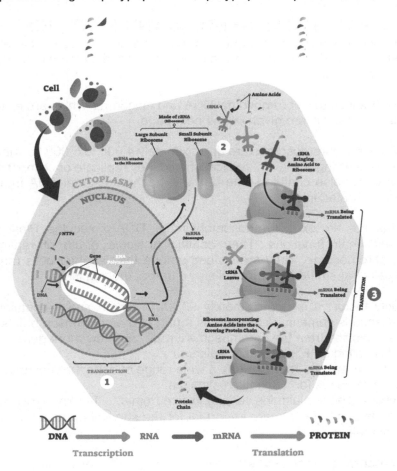

17. REGULATION OF GENE EXPRESSION

Concepts
1. Prokaryotic and eukaryotic genomes are organized in different manner and their expressions are controlled differently even though there are considerable similarities.
2. Genes are regulated by proteins that bind to regulatory sequences that are upstream or downstream of the transcribed sequences.
3. Prokaryotic genes are organized in units called as operons and they are regulated by metabolites binding to proteins that recognize and bind to operators.
4. Eukaryotes have complex regulation of gene expression due to their multicellular nature and complex functions.
5. Regulation of gene expression in eukaryotes occurs at multiple levels such as transcriptional, post-transcriptional, translational and post-translational level.

Outline
I.   Bacterial Genome and Genetics
II. Regulation of Gene Expression in Prokaryotes
III. Structure of Eukaryotic Genome and Genes
IV. Regulation of Eukaryotic Gene Expression
V.   Gene regulation and Development

I. BACTERIAL GENOME AND GENETICS

Bacteria and viruses have been excellent model systems to study molecular genetics because of their simple and small **genome**, rapid multiplication in a short time period, and the large genetic variations that occur within a selected population.

A. The **bacterial genome** includes chromosomal DNA and episomes, which are extrachromosomal DNA present as plasmid(s). The details are given on the next page.

1. Chromosomes: Bacterial chromosomes are approximately 4,000 to 5,000 kb with about 3,000 genes. The chromosome contains a single origin of replication and they replicate once in 20 minutes prior to each cell division. Chromosomes also contain some of the extrachromosomal DNA from plasmids and viral DNAs that have been integrated into them.

2. Plasmid DNA: Plasmids are extrachromosomal circular DNA molecules. Plasmids vary in size, the genes they carry, and their functions. They contain a single origin of replication and replicate independently of the chromosome. They are divided among the daughter cells randomly during binary fission, or are specifically transmitted to other cells by different mechanisms.

a. F-plasmid: (Fertility factor) It is approximately 93 kb in length and it contains genes that confer "maleness." The F-plasmid is sometimes present as a part of the chromosome. It is transmitted through sexual mating. When it excises from the chromosome it may carry few more genes, it may be as long as 100 kb or more and it is called an **F'** plasmid or episome.
b. R-plasmid: (Resistance factor). This includes a wide range of extrachromosomal DNA varying in size from 3 to 117 kb that carry genes for antibiotic resistance.
c. Colicinogenic factors: These plasmids varying in size from 4 to 141 kb carry genes coding for toxins (colicin). The R-plasmids and C-factors are important for the survival of bacteria. These may also carry some genes for sexual mating.

3. Transposable elements: (transposons): These are mobile genetic elements, or "jumping genes," which can transpose from one part of a chromosome to another part or a different chromosome. These were first characterized in maize by Barbara McClintock and later they were found to be present in bacteria and other organisms. The different types of transposons in bacteria are listed below:
a. Insertion sequences (IS) are simple transposons varying in size from 768 (IS1) to about 1537 (IS50R) bases. They contain inverted repeats at their terminals and they carry enzymes called transposases to move from one place to another in the chromosome.
b. Complex transposons contain inverted repeats at their terminals in addition to the antibiotic resistance

genes they carry. They are also longer, varying from 3100 (Tn903; kanamycin resistance) to 9300 (Tn10; tetracycline resistance) base pairs in length.

These transposable elements recognize a specific DNA sequence in the target region (the site they are moving into), cut the DNA, and insert themselves using the enzyme transposase. These elements are critical in generating new combinations of genes, mutations, and ultimately the microevolution of bacteria to survive challenging environments.

B. Transfer and recombination of bacterial DNA:

Bacterial DNA is introduced from one bacterium to another by conjugation, transduction or transformation.

1. Conjugation: It is the sexual mating of bacteria through F-pili (plural; pilus = singular) and the genes present in the F-factor are transferred from an F⁺ bacteria to an F⁻ bacteria. The proteins for F-pili are coded by genes present in the F-factor. Bacterial conjugation was discovered by Lederberg and Tatum in 1946 when they were analyzing bacterial mutants (see later) which transferred genes necessary for certain amino acid biosynthesis through F-pili. The F-factor is transmitted as a single strand from one bacterium into another bacterium through the F-pilus. After the transfer, it is converted into dsDNA, and it may exist as an F- episome or be integrated into the chromosome (as F-factor). When it is integrated into the chromosome the bacteria is referred to as high frequency recombination (hfr) strain. If it exists as an F-episome in bacteria already containing an F-factor in the chromosome, the genes present in these two are allelic to each other, and they can recombine, resulting in new genotypes.

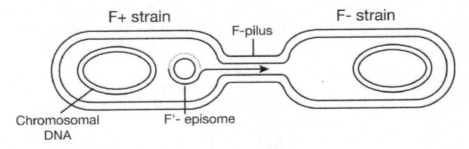

The F-factor in chromosomes of an hfr strain sometimes separate from the chromosome and get transferred to an F- bacteria. This process is also referred to as sexduction.

2. Transduction: Transfer of a part of a chromosome from one bacterium to another mediated through a phage is referred to as transduction. The transduction may be general, wherein random fragments from bacterial chromosomes are transmitted by phages or specific, in which certain sequences are always carried by phages from one strain to another. Transduction is also referred to as transfection, which is an experimental method used to introduce DNA fragments into bacteria using phages as vectors (to carry the DNA and replicate in a bacteria). Transfection is an efficient method to transform bacteria, express foreign genes in bacteria, and for DNA library construction, which are explained in a later chapter.

3. Transformation: Introduction of DNA from an external medium into the bacteria. You may recall Fredrick Griffith's experiment followed by the experiment of Avery et al., showing that bacteria isolated from a S-strain can be used to transform the R-strain. Salt solutions, heat shock, freezing and thawing, and electroporation are some of the methods used to transform bacterial cells.

II. REGULATION OF GENE EXPRESSION IN PROKARYOTES

Gene expression refers to the synthesis of RNA from a DNA template. The RNA may code for mRNA, rRNA, or tRNA. Broadly speaking, gene expression also includes the translation of mRNA(s) into specific protein(s) resulting in a specific phenotype(s). Gene expression may be constitutive or regulated. Constitutive genes are always expressed without much regulation. The genes that are vital for the routine functioning of the organism are expressed continuously. However, some genes are expressed in a tightly regulated manner. It is important to understand the structure of bacterial genes to understand their regulation.

Bacterial genes are organized into units called operons. An operon constitutes the coding sequences of the genes in that unit, a promoter, and an operator. The promoter and operator determine the accuracy and amount of transcription respectively.

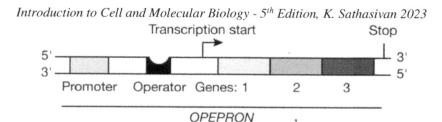

The DNA sequence of the promoter alone can alter the level of gene transcripts. As we saw earlier, bacterial RNA is polycistronic, i.e., many transcripts are made from one operon simultaneously as a single mRNA in a single transcription. This is an efficient way of controlling the transcription process. The operator serves as the on-off switch to regulate the transcription in response to environmental stimuli. The operons may be either induced (inducible or positive regulation) or repressed (negative regulation).

A. Inducible operon: Inducible operons are mostly turned off, and they are turned on only when necessary. E.g., lac operon. The lac operon is induced under two situations—namely when lactose is present with glucose or alone. When lactose is present along with glucose, the cells prefer glucose. However, the expression of genes for lactose-utilizing enzymes is activated by removing a repressor that is bound to the operator of the lac operon. The lactose binds to the repressor molecule, and the operon is derepressed to start transcription.

Further activation: If there is no glucose and only lactose is present, it results in an increase of cyclicAMP (cAMP) levels in the cells. The cAMP binds to a catabolite activator protein (CAP) and that binds to the promoter to further enhance the activity of the lac operon much more than the basal level at derepression alone.

A. Lactose absent

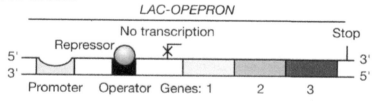

B. Lactose and glucose present

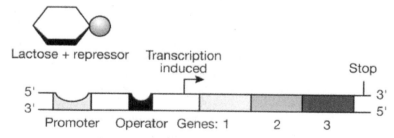

B. Lactose present but no glucose

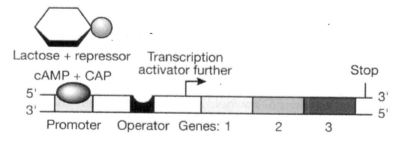

Inducible operons are normally present to control catabolic pathways used to break down compounds.

B. Repressible operon

These are used for anabolic pathways to synthesize compounds. Repressible operons are mostly turned on, and they are turned off when not needed. Example: Trp-operon to synthesize tryptophan. The enzymes in the Trp biosynthetic pathway are expressed only when Trp is absent. When trp is absent a repressor protein is inactive and it does not bind to the operator to repress transcription. When sufficient levels of Trp are made, it binds to the repressor molecule and makes it an active repressor that now binds to the operator and stops transcription. This is similar to the feedback inhibition of enzymes except that it occurs at the gene level. Trp acts as a corepressor and controls the transcription of genes in its operon.

The regulation of the Trp operon is shown below:

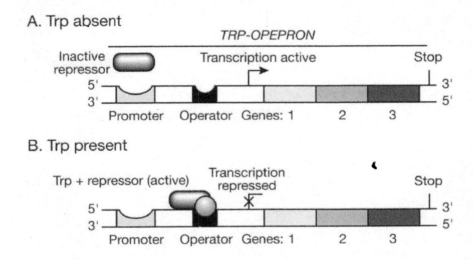

Gene regulation is also controlled by other proteins such as sigma factors, which can bind to the regulatory elements of bacteria and activate transcription. There are several types of sigma factors and other DNA-binding proteins that regulate prokaryotic gene expression. Such factors can transmit environmental signals to the genes to express the needed proteins immediately in response to the stimulus.

III.   STRUCTURE OF EUKARYOTIC GENOME AND GENES

A. Genome size: The chromosomal DNA inside the nucleus is dispersed as chromatin during most of the cell cycle. The double helix of DNA wraps around histone proteins to form the nucleosomes, which condense further to make chromatin as explained in Chapter 9. Eukaryotic chromosomes are linear molecules with defined ends called telomeres. The amount of DNA and number of chromosomes varies greatly among eukaryotes, so does the DNA length and number of genes. A rough idea about the number of genes in eukaryotes vs. prokaryotes might suggest a general trend of increasing size with the increasing complexities of genomes. However, genome size is not necessarily a representation of organismal complexity. For example, humans contain 46 chromosomes, whereas some crabs contain as many as 200 and some ferns up to 1,000. It is the sequence of DNA and the proteins coded by them, and not the amount of DNA alone, that determines how complex a species is. Much of the apparently excessive DNA is made of repetitive sequences that generally do not code for proteins.

B. Repetitive DNA: Most of the DNA in eukaryotic genomes, in contrast to prokaryotic genomes is made of DNA sequences that do not code for any RNA or protein. About 10% to 25% of higher eukaryotic DNA is made up of repetitive DNA with 5 to 10 bases repeated 1,000s of times. Such repetitive DNA can be identified by reannealing denatured DNA. As we saw in the structure of the DNA double helix, dsDNA can be denatured and renatured by heating and cooling. When they renature, the complementary sequences base pair to anneal. Based on how fast DNA reanneals, one can determine if it consists of highly repetitive or unique sequences. Based on such studies and others (explained in Chapter 15), unique sequences or single copy genes can be detected. Repetitive sequences are found near telomeres and are useful in the DNA replication process because they fold onto themselves to provide a 3'-OH group for DNA synthesis.

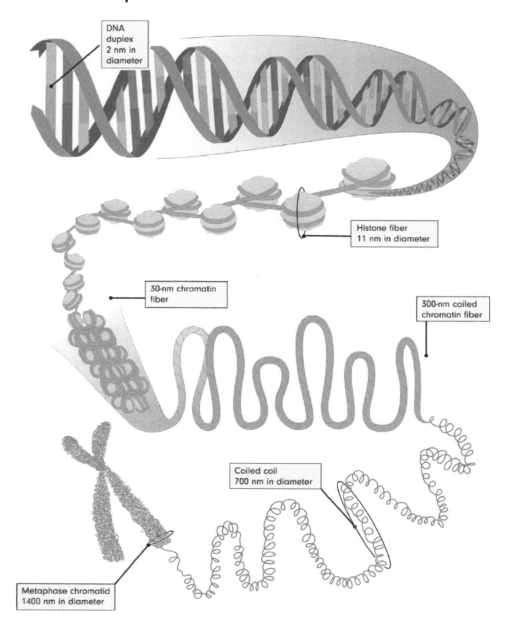

C. Multiple gene families: Some genes are present in a single or a few copies, whereas some other genes are present in large numbers and are organized into gene families. This is the result of gene duplication during crossing over, or a result of transposable elements translocating a gene from one chromosome to another, or to a different location on the same chromosome. Genes essential for the survival of an organism are highly duplicated during evolution. Such duplicated copies of genes may mutate and evolve independently. Sometimes, they lose their regulatory sequences (promoter and other cis-elements), and are not expressed at all. Such genes are called pseudogenes. The multigene family members may be located together on a chromosome, or spread out in different chromosomes. Such families can be detected by DNA-DNA hybridization techniques explained in the next chapter. The expression of multigene family members is regulated by common cis-acting elements recognized by common trans-acting factors specific for that gene family. This is referred to **coordinated gene expression**. Globin genes coding for the subunits of hemoglobin are an example of a multigene family.

IV.   REGULATION OF GENE EXPRESSION IN EUKARYOTES

Eukaryotic genes are organized differently from those of prokaryotes. The messages of eukaryotic genes are monocistronic (one mRNA per transcription to make one protein), and many genes contain intervening sequences (introns) that must be removed and exons that must be spliced. Additionally, processed mRNA contains a 5' G-cap and 3' poly (A) tail. Similar to prokaryotes, there are some genes expressed constantly (constitutive genes) and some are highly regulated in their expression. Eukaryotic genes are regulated by a set of regulatory DNA sequences (collectively known as cis-acting elements), which are recognized by trans-acting factors. This concept was introduced in Chapter 11. Here, we will see how eukaryotic gene expression is regulated at various levels. In prokaryotes, transcription and translation can occur simultaneously, for there is no nucleus to separate transcription from translation and no introns to be removed. In eukaryotes, gene expression can be regulated at the transcriptional level, posttranscriptional level, translational level, or posttranslational level.

A. Transcriptional regulation:

The rate of transcription is regulated at the gene level with different mechanisms operating for long-term and short-term controls.

Long-term control: The chromosomes are condensed during cell division, but gradually uncoil again to become dispersed as chromatin. However, a portion of chromatin remains condensed as heterochromatin, which is not readily accessible by RNA polymerases and other proteins. Some regions are more diffuse, existing as euchromatin, and are accessible for transcription. E.g., one of the X-chromosomes in females is inactivated and such condensed chromosomes are called Barr bodies.

Another way to control transcription on selected chromosomes is to methylate the DNA. Methylation is done by DNA methylases such as deoxy cytosine methylase (DCM) or deoxy adenosine methylase (DAM) which add methyl groups to the C and A bases respectively. DNA methylation at the C and A nucleotides results in the prevention of such regions from being transcribed. In humans as much as 5% of DNA is methylated and only about 3% to 5% of genes are actively transcribed at any given time. DNA methylation also helps DNA polymerase to distinguish the old strand from the new strand. In bacteria, DNA methylation is critical for recognizing cellular versus viral DNA. The pattern and amount of methylation varies with species. Acetylation of histone proteins activates gene expression.

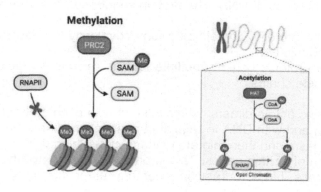

DNA Methylation inhibits gene expression

DNA Acetylation stimulates gene expression

2. ***Short-term control:*** Some regions of chromosomes are actively transcribed as transcription puffs. Such regions can be easily seen in the large multistranded polytene chromosomes in the salivary gland cells of *Drosophila larva*. Transcription of genes in eukaryotes is controlled by the interaction between transcription factors and the regulatory elements on the genes. The regulatory elements include the promoter, which is closer to and upstream of the start site, and enhancers or repressors, which may be upstream or downstream from the start site. The promoter is present at a relatively fixed distance, whereas other elements may be present close to or far from the start site. The structure of a eukaryotic gene and its regulatory sequences are shown in the figure below.

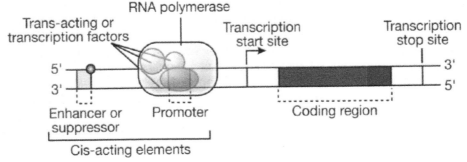

The trans-acting proteins recognize specific cis-acting elements on the DNA by binding to a specific DNA sequence and inducing or inhibiting transcription. Some factors directly bind to RNA polymerase or other DNA binding proteins, and affect transcription through protein-protein interaction. Transcription factors have unique secondary structures to recognize the DNA, and can be grouped into the following categories:

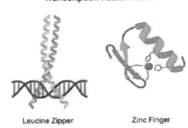

Transcription Factor Motifs

Leucine Zipper   Zinc Finger

a. Helix-turn-helix proteins: These proteins contain an alpha-helix, beta-turn, and alpha-helix secondary structures that fit within the grooves of DNA. The protein sequences can vary and thus bind to different DNA sequences.

b. Zinc finger proteins: The proteins contain zinc ions covalently bonded to certain residues, which protrude as fingers and recognize DNA.

c. Leucine zippers: These proteins contain multiple leucine residues, which interact because of the hydrophobic nature of their side chains.

All these DNA binding proteins act as dimers, which interact with each other along these motifs (unique secondary/tertiary strictures) and with DNA to regulate transcription. Some hormones can bind to these transcription factors in cytoplasm and then migrate to the nucleus, bind with specific cis-acting elements, and activate the transcription of certain genes. This is one mechanism by which hormones secreted by the glands travel to other cells, binds to specific receptors, enter the cells, interact with transcription factors, and activate the genes.

B. Posttranscriptional Regulation

This type of regulation is limited compared to transcriptional regulation. Post-transcriptional regulation involves differential processing of the mRNA transcript or relative stabilities of mRNA.

a. Alternate splicing: This happens during mRNA processing, wherein introns are removed and exons spliced. Some mRNAs are processed differently to yield different proteins. For example, exons 1, 2, and 3 may be joined to form one kind of protein and exons 1 and 3 alone joined to make another kind of protein.

b. mRNA stability: On the other hand, some mRNAs have unique sequences at the 5' or 3' NTRs (non-translated regions) that affect their stability in the cytoplasm. Some mRNAs are long-lived, for up to several days, and some are short-lived, lasting only a few minutes after transcription. When mRNAs are long-lived, it allows the translation to continue for a longer time. The mRNA stability is altered by RNA binding proteins which may tag the mRNA for degradation or degrade the mRNA themselves.

C. Translational Regulation

Translation in eukaryotes occurs in the cytoplasm and it involves several proteins known as initiation factors and elongation factors. Also, depending on the sequence of the ribosome recognition site on the mRNA, mRNA can be translated more efficiently or less efficiently. Another translational control is to block translation of processed mRNA until the need arises.

Examples of translational regulation are given below:

a. mRNA storage: Many processed mRNAs are stored in the nucleus of an egg prior to fertilization and are translated after fertilization and during embryonic development. This control may be exerted by not modifying the 5' G-cap or not having the right initiation factor present until the cells are ready to translate such mRNAs.

b. Hormonal regulation: An alternate mechanism involves hormonal action. For example, the casein mRNA is translated 25 times more efficiently in the presence of a hormone prolactin to produce the milk protein casein. Prolactin is made when the animal is ready for lactation.

c. Effect of cofactor on translation. Another example of translational control is observed in the synthesis and assembly of globins and hemes to make hemoglobin. Hemoglobins consist of two α-globins, two β-globins, and 4 small heme molecules (cofactors). When heme molecules accumulate, they increase the translational efficiency of globin mRNAs.

D. Posttranslational Regulation.

This is the last stage of controlling gene expression at the protein level. Some examples of posttranslational modifications or processing of proteins were discussed in Chapter 11. The posttranslational processing results in functional proteins in most situations automatically. However, in some situations it is used as a regulatory mechanism. Examples of such regulation include the following:

a. Zymogen activation: Some proteins are first made in inactive forms and later they are converted to active forms. For example, insulin is first made as proinsulin, and then it is converted to insulin to become active.

b. Selective targeting: For membrane proteins and proteins targeted for specific organelles to be active, they should be in the right place. A segment of proteins, normally at the NH_2-terminal, determines the protein's target site. The protein may then be transported through Golgi vesicles to the right membrane or organelle. Once it reaches its destination, the target peptide (also called the leader sequence or signal sequence) is removed and the protein is active. Sometimes if the protein does not reach the target, often because of defective target signaling, the protein remains in the cytoplasm and is degraded. E.g., the chloride channel protein in cystic fibrosis is mutated and does not reach the target.

c. Chemical modification of proteins to be active or inactive. We have seen examples of phosphorylation to make a particular protein active or inactive. In the cell cycle, cyclin levels are modulated by phosphorylation and the activation of proteases that will degrade cyclin. In the Na^+/K^+ pump, the transport of Na^+ out and K^+ in is facilitated by phosphorylation and dephosphorylation. Phosphorylation happens at the -OH group of serine, threonine, and tyrosine.

d. Glycoslylation: Many membrane proteins are glycosylated after translation in the Golgi apparatus or rough ER. The short oligosaccharides are added either to serine or threonine at their -OH group (O-linked glycosylation) or to asparagine at the $-NH_2$ group (N-linked glycosylation). Glycosylation reduces the chances of degradation by proteases and it facilitates signal transduction.

V. GENE REGULATION AND DEVELOPMENT

The program for the development of an organism is encoded in genes. All multicellular organisms start as a single cell: a zygote in sexual reproduction or an embryonic cell in asexual reproduction. The single cell having the potential to become a whole new organism is called **totipotency**. Totipotency is observed in several types of cells in plants, whereas it is mainly in the zygotes of animal cells. Totipotent cells undergo division, differentiation, and growth to become a fully developed organism with different types of cells, tissues, and organs. Interplay of genes, proteins, internal chemical signals, such as hormones, and the external environment in this developmental process is complex and we are only beginning to understand such processes in higher animals. It is beyond the scope of this course to cover developmental processes of multicellular organisms. However, these examples of changes at the genetic level give some idea as to how the developmental process may be regulated.

A. Genomic rearrangement: As the cells divide and develop some genes are rearranged to express certain genes in a variable manner. For example, immunoglobulin (antibody) genes coding for four different peptides can rearrange themselves to shuffle their genes in order to create a wide diversity of the proteins resulting from them. Another example of gene rearrangement is in the yeast mating type involving a- and □□-types, which can be reshuffled to create new mating types in alternate generations. If the arrangement is □□□-a, it results in the □ type and if the a-gene is copied and used to replace the middle a gene, it becomes □-a-a and results in the a-type.

Transposable elements: Another mechanism to rearrange the genes is through transposable elements. Transposable elements provide the opportunity for various genes to be moved from one place to another. Sometimes, the genes are interrupted and inactivated by transposable elements. Transposable elements were first characterized in corn by Barbara McClintock at the Cold Spring Harbor Laboratory. Transposable elements in eukaryotes vary from the prokaryotic transposons in that they do not exist independently, but move with RNA as an intermediate and lack antibiotic genes. These elements can be integrated randomly or in hot spots of chromosomes. The details of their transposition and their roles in eukaryotes are not well known. One reason suggested for their existence is to create variation among the gene pool so that organisms can adapt to varying environments.

B. Master genes controlling development: There are certain genes called homeotic genes, which control a wide array of other genes involved in developmental. Such homeotic genes were first characterized in *Drosophila* in which mutants of altered physical traits, such as antenna in place of eyes, were isolated. These master genes or homoeotic genes mostly code for transcription factors that can bind to a common regulatory sequence on several genes involved in the developmental process.

C. Gene Amplification: Sometimes certain genes are duplicated several times to amplify their number, so that enough copies of mRNAs can be produced. The genes for ribosomal RNA are amplified at earlier stages of development so that there are enough copies of rRNA genes to make rRNA for ribosomes and mRNA for ribosomal proteins. In some cases, the genes for herbicide resistance are amplified to survive the chemical.

D. Tissue specific gene expression: During and after development, genes are expressed in a tissue-specific manner to facilitate the function of different cell or tissue types. For example, leaf tissues in a plant will make proteins for photosynthesis and storage tissues in the seed will make storage proteins. This tissue specific expression of genes is controlled by the transcription factors being selectively active in specific tissues.

Summary of gene expression in Eukaryotes

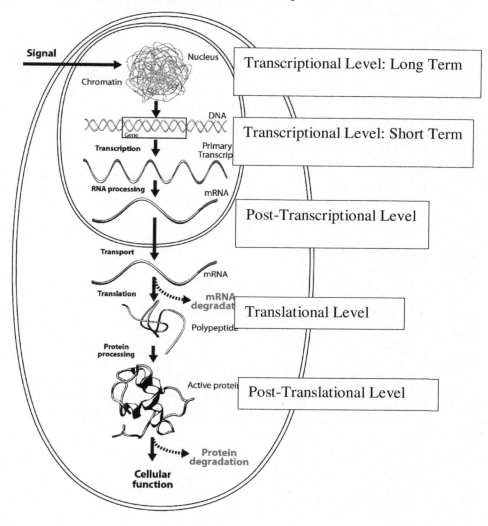

Signal

Nucleus

Chromatin

DNA

Gene

Transcription

Primary Transcript

RNA processing

mRNA

Transport

mRNA

Translation

mRNA degradation

Polypeptide

Protein processing

Active protein

Protein degradation

Cellular function

Transcriptional Level: Long Term

Transcriptional Level: Short Term

Post-Transcriptional Level

Translational Level

Post-Translational Level

Outline

I.   Basic Tools and Techniques
II. Gene Isolation, Characterization, and Transfer
III. Application of Genetic Engineering to Humans, Animals, and Agriculture
IV. Bioethics and Safety Issues

I. BASIC TOOLS AND TECHNIQUES

Recombinant DNA technology is based on the central dogma of molecular biology that DNA makes RNA makes protein and the fact that if you modify the gene you can modify the protein. Recombinant DNA techniques are used to study molecular aspects of life and to apply the information in a constructive and ethical manner to benefit life through academic and commercial research. Recombinant DNA technology refers to a set of techniques used to isolate, recombine, transfer, and express genes or DNA for further study. Like any other technology, recombinant DNA work is dependent on certain basic tools such as enzymes and plasmids, and certain techniques are essential. A selected list of such tools and techniques are briefly described below.

A. Common enzymes used in molecular biology:

1. Restriction endonucleases are enzymes isolated from prokaryotes that can recognize a specific DNA sequence and cleave the DNA at that recognition site or another place. There are different types of restriction endonucleases present in prokaryotic cells to protect them from invading viruses and foreign DNA. Some are generic, i.e., cut DNA nonspecifically, and some are specific. Among the specific restriction enzymes, type I and type III recognize at one site and cleave at another place. Additionally, type I and III have methylase activity. Type II restriction endonucleases are the most commonly used restriction enzymes without methylase activity, and they recognize and cleave at a particular DNA sequence.

The enzymes are named after the bacterium they are isolated from. E.g., the enzyme EcoRI, isolated from *Escherichia coli,* can recognize and cut DNA with the sequence 5'-GAATTC-3'.

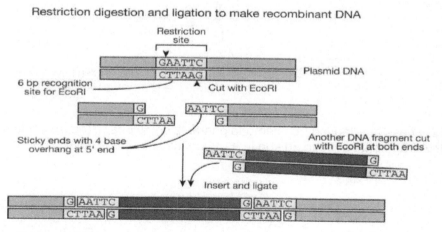

Restriction digestion and ligation to make recombinant DNA

This is a six base pair recognition enzyme. Other enzymes can recognize four base pairs or longer. Once the restriction enzyme cuts the DNA, they may leave an overhang of four base pairs at the 5' or 3' end or they may leave a blunt end. The 5' or 3' overhangs are called sticky ends, because they can anneal with similar sticky ends based on their complementarities. Such enzymes that cut DNA at specific sites are needed to create recombinant DNA molecules.

2. DNA polymerase: DNA polymerases are used to make DNA in vitro. DNA synthesis is accomplished by providing a DNA template, suitable primers (oligonucleotides, 15 to 30 base long, DNA primer complementary to template), dNTPs, a DNA polymerase, Mg^{++}, and a suitable buffer with the optimum pH and ionic condition. Commonly used DNA polymerases are obtained from *E. coli,* T7 bacteriophage, or thermostable bacteria and used for various applications, such as DNA synthesis, DNA sequencing, and polymerase chain reactions.

3. DNA ligase: As we saw in DNA replication, DNA ligase can catalyze the covalent bonding of the 3' and 5' ends of two DNA strands. This is used to connect two DNA strands having blunt ends or complementary sticky ends created by restriction enzymes to make a recombinant DNA molecule. E.g., T4 DNA ligase obtained from the T4 phage is one the most commonly used ligases.

4. Reverse transcriptase (RT): Reverse transcriptase is an RNA-dependent DNA polymerase, i.e., it uses an RNA template to make a complementary DNA (cDNA). This is used in cDNA library construction and to amplify DNA from RNA. The commonly used RTs are isolated from viruses such as AMV (an avian virus) and MMLV (a marine virus). Some thermostable DNA polymerases also have reverse transcriptase activity under different salt conditions.

B. Vectors and hosts:

Vectors are the DNA vehicles that can carry genes from one organism to another, and allow it to replicate in a particular host. *E. coli* is one of the most commonly used host systems in recombinant DNA. Others include yeast, plant cells, and animal cells maintained in cell cultures. Some commonly used vectors are plasmid or phage based.

1. Plasmid vectors: Plasmids are double-stranded circular DNA molecules with an origin of replication, an antibiotic marker gene for selection, and restrictions sites that are unique and that can be used to insert a DNA fragment to be cloned. Cloning refers to the process of making multiple identical copies of a particular DNA fragment or a gene after making the recombinant DNA and introducing it into a suitable bacterial host (transformation). Plasmid vectors are used to clone genes of relatively small size (100 bp to 15 kbp) and they are relatively less efficient than phage vectors. However, they are easier to handle and are more stable to maintain than phage vectors. E.g., pBluescript is one of the commonly used plasmid vector.

A basic plasmid vector:

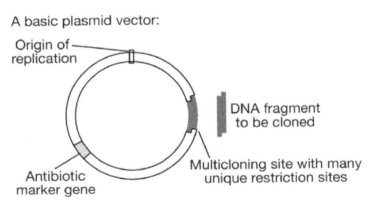

2. Phage vectors: These are derived from lambda phage, a small phage (approximately 48 kbp) that can accommodate DNA fragments of 10 to 20 kbp in a region that is nonessential.

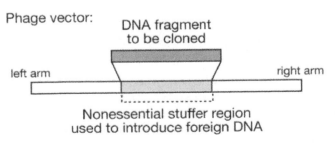

The nonessential region in the middle of the phage is removed and foreign DNA is inserted. Then the phage is used to infect the *E. coli* host (transfection) to introduce the gene and to multiply it. Transfection is more efficient than transformation.

C. Basic techniques:
1. Gel electrophoresis:

This is used to fractionate DNA or RNA fragments based on their size. The negative charges on the DNA or RNA make them migrate toward the anode (+) through tiny pores in the agarose or polyacrylamide gel. The molecules migrate depending on their size and electric voltage in the system. Larger molecules move slowly and smaller molecules move quickly. The higher the voltage, the faster they move. Agarose gels are used to fractionate DNA or RNA. These are easier to make, but the size fractionation is approximate. Polyacrylamide gels are used to fractionate proteins and DNA. Polyacrylamide gels are relatively harder to make but provide better resolution of size. The accuracy of polyacrylamide gels varies from approximate fractionation of proteins to accurate separation of DNA in DNA-sequencing gels depending upon the thickness, length, and the size of the molecules being separated.

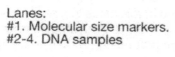
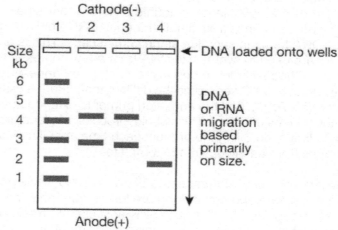

2. Restriction fragment length polymorphism (RFLP): This is a technique commonly used to identify differences in the restriction pattern of a specific gene or DNA region between several individuals of a species or several related species. The DNA is cut by selected restriction enzymes and fractionated on an agarose gel. The differences in the sizes of the fragments obtained from the restriction digestion are used to identify the relationship between individuals. For example, samples 1 and 2 (in lanes 2 and 3) in the above figure show identical restriction patterns but sample 3 (in lane 4) is different. It shows that sample 3 is from a similar gene which has a mutation in the restriction sites used to cut the DNA.

3. Radiolabeling DNA fragments: To identify a DNA fragment in an organism, it is important to label DNA with a radioisotope or fluorescent label that can be detected using X-ray film.

The commonly used isotopes are ^{35}S or ^{32}P to label DNA or RNA. These isotopes are used in reactions to synthesize DNA or RNA and are incorporated into the strands during such synthesis. The following diagram shows the locations of such labels. The ^{32}P is incorporated either in the alpha position or gamma position depending on the purpose. Radiolabeling is used in DNA sequencing, Southern and Northern techniques, as explained below.

4. DNA Sequencing: The dideoxy chain termination method was originally developed by Sanger. DNA sequencing is done by doing an in vitro DNA synthesis using a DNA template, a specific primer, dNTPs, and DNA polymerase extending the new strand of DNA from the primer in a suitable buffer. The sequence of the complementary strand is obtained by stopping the chain extension by randomly incorporating dideoxynucleotides labeled with fluorescent molecules. Each of the nucleotides G, A, T, C are labeled with different color labels. The DNA fragments of random length are size fractionated by polyacrylamide electrophoresis and the sequence is determined by the fluorescent label attached to each dideoxy nucleotide in an automated sequencing method. The manual method is a little more complex. An alternate method using chemicals to sequence DNA was developed by Maxim and Gilbert.

5. Polymerase chain reaction (PCR).
This method is used to amplify large amounts of DNA from small amounts of samples. This is used extensively in cloning new genes from small amounts of RNA or DNA and in forensics to identify a suspect by amplifying the DNA found in samples at the crime scene. This is an in vitro DNA synthesis reaction, in which two primers are used to synthesize DNA from a few copies of template using a thermostable DNA polymerase. This method includes a denaturation step, an annealing step, and an extension step. The denaturation step done at 90°C separates the dsDNA template. The ssDNA anneals with the primer during the annealing step (55-70°C), and the annealed primer is extended by the DNA polymerase incorporating dNTPs during the extension step. This whole process of denaturation, annealing, and extension is repeated about 32 times, doubling the product each time, resulting in approximately up to 1 billion copies of the DNA fragment from each copy of the template.

6 CRISPR: (Clustered Regularly Interspersed Short Palindromic Repeats). These DNA sequence repeats are widely found in bacteria and archae and are left as remnants from viral infection of these organisms. These repeats are recognized by Cas (CRISPR associated proteins) and cleaved from the genome for degradation. This system is used for specifically removing an unwanted sequence from other organisms including humans where one can potentially remove any remnants of HIV or other defective genes. There are many ethical questions of genetically modifying humans but it has vast potential in the genetic improvement of plants and animals.

II. GENE ISOLATION, CHARACTERIZATION, AND TRANSFER

Gene isolation is done by construction of genomic DNA libraries or cDNA libraries. The procedures are briefly mentioned here. Genomic clones are DNA fragments containing the gene, including introns, exons, promoters, and other noncoding regions. The cDNA includes only the coding region of a gene, because it is derived from a processed mRNA through reverse transcription.

A. Isolating genes and the study of genomics
Genes are isolated by first making a **genomic DNA or cDNA library** or from randomly amplified fragments through PCR. DNA library refers to a collection of several different DNA fragments constructed in a vector (plasmid or phage vectors) and maintained in a bacterial host. The whole library is screened using a radioactively labeled probe (a DNA fragment from a related gene or a synthetic DNA fragment based on protein sequences). The probe and the library DNA are denatured by alkali and renatured by neutralizing with an acid. During neutralization, specific clones which are highly complementary to the probe will anneal with the probe (called hybridization). These clones, present in individual bacterial colonies, are identified through the radioactivity of the probe and are isolated for further characterization. Once isolated, their DNA is isolated and sequenced.

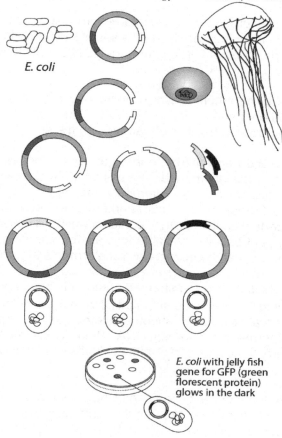

E. coli

E. coli with jelly fish gene for GFP (green florescent protein) glows in the dark

In **genome projects,** the entire DNA sequence of the organism is completely sequenced. Prior to sequencing the entire genome, it has to be physically mapped using **genetic markers** that are associated with specific phenotypes and or sequences. **Genomics** refers to the analysis of the DNA and protein sequences. The analysis could be simply at the structural level (structural genomics) or at the functional level (functional genomics). Structural genomics includes computer analysis of DNA and protein sequences. Collection and analysis of biological sequence information is referred to as **bioinformatics**. Availability of extensive amounts of information and analysis of their structure and function will eventually lead to a detailed understanding of the role that genes play in shaping an organism or a species. With the advances in automated sequencing and analysis, this process will advance at a rapid rate in the coming decades.

B. Characterizing genes
Once genes are isolated, they need to be sequenced; the sequence is compared against known DNA and protein sequences in the DNA data banks. Then the genomic structure of the gene and its expression needs to be studied by Southern and Northern techniques.

1. Southern hybridization:
This refers to hybridizing a labeled DNA probe to the target DNA sequences immobilized on a nylon membrane. The DNA bound to the membrane has been size fractionated on an agarose gel, denatured, and then transferred to the membrane through either capillary action or electric transfer. Since this was discovered by E.M. Southern, it was named after him. The other methods were then named Northern (RNA-RNA hybridization) and Western (protein-antibody recognition) as variants of Southern. Southern hybridization analysis is used to study the genome organization of a particular gene and determine the approximate number of copies of a specific gene. It is also used in RFLP analysis to find out if the restriction pattern of a particular gene differs between individuals. DNA-DNA hybridization techniques are commonly used in library screening and to find out if a particular gene is present in a genome or not.

2. Northern hybridization: This involves hybridizing a labeled DNA probe with size-fractionated RNA immobilized on a nylon membrane. This method is used to determine the RNA levels for a particular gene at different stages or in different tissues or organs of an organism.

3. Western hybridization involves protein-antibody interaction. A specific protein (antigen) is recognized first by a primary antibody which is then recognized by a secondary antibody conjugated to a fluorescent probe or an enzyme. The enzyme can convert a chromogenic substrate into a colored substance for the detection.

4. Microarray analysis helps in determining which genes are expressed among a group of several thousand genes that are placed on a small microscopic slide. The probe used to study the expression is fluorescent-labeled mRNA hybridized to fixed DNA samples on the slide.

C. Gene Transfer methods: Gene transfer from one organism to another is an important technique in the construction, maintenance, replication, and expression of recombinant DNA in the transgenic organism. Such transformed organisms are commonly referred to as GMO—genetically modified organisms. To confirm the transformation, antibiotic marker genes are used to select for transformants that have become resistant to certain antibiotics that would normally kill untransformed cells. The following techniques summarize the different options available for transforming different types of organisms. The efficiency of transformation is measured by how many transformants are obtained per μg of DNA.

1. Bacterial transformation. Bacteria are transformed commonly by simply treating them with $CaCl_2$ or similar salts in solution and mixing them with recombinant DNA. A more efficient method is to electroporate the bacteria with DNA. Electroporation involves shooting a temporary short pulse of electricity through the bacteria, which then becomes permeable to foreign DNA. Alternatively, bacteria can be transfected using recombinant phages, which carry the desired DNA along with its essential DNA. This is used to construct DNA libraries.

2. Plant transformation: Plant transformation is done using cells that are embryonic or totipotent, which can be cultured under special conditions to regenerate completely new transformed plants. The most commonly used method of transformation of plants is by employing a bacterium called *Agrobacterium tumefaciens,* which can transfer a recombinant DNA plasmid into the plant cell and stably integrate it into its chromosome. This method works well for most dicots but monocots and some dicots are more difficult to transform. For such plants, an alternate method called particle gun bombardment is used. In this method gold particles coated with the recombinant DNA are physically shot into the cells using particle guns ("gene guns") specially designed for this purpose. Similar to bacterial transformants, the plant cells that are transformed are selected for using an antibiotic.

3. Animal transformation: Isolated animal cells maintained in culture are transformed by salt-mediated transformation, transfection using phages, or electroporation. Sometimes microinjection is used to introduce DNA into large cells such as frog oocytes or other egg cells. Transformation of whole animals is done at the embryonic stage or at the egg or sperm level followed by fertilization, and then they are impregnated into a surrogate mother to regenerate a transformed animal.

III. APPLICATIONS OF RECOMBINANT DNA TECHNOLOGY

A. Plants: Plants are the first major organisms to see a vast application of recombinant DNA technology because of the ease of transformation and limited ethical issues involved other than safety issues. The current applications include but are not limited to herbicide resistance, insect resistance, disease resistance, and improved storage quality. The transgenic plants are being approved by the FDA (Food and Drug Administration) and are already showing up in the market place. Examples are Flavr-Savr tomato with long storage life, golden rice with high beta-carotene content, insect resistant, and herbicide-resistant crops.

B. Animals: Genetically engineering animals is not a major ethical issue and some applications of making novel proteins in animals have been developed by introducing genes at early embryonic stages. Some hormones are developed by recombinant DNA techniques to increase milk production (e.g., bovine somatotropin; BST) or meat production. Vaccines are developed for severe diseases that can be difficult to treat.

C. Humans: This is a rapidly changing field with newer and newer applications being developed and going through approval processes. Some applications include identification of genetic diseases by discovering the specific genes involved in genetic diseases, diagnostics of diseases or infection such as HIV, development of recombinant vaccines by engineering various antigens in one plasmid to develop multiple vaccines, and gene therapy techniques to rectify genetic errors. DNA detection techniques are extensively used in forensics and in paternity testing. Additionally, identification of new viruses such as the SARS (Severe Acute Respiratory Syndrome) virus is becoming routine with the advent of DNA technologies. Other proteins that are important for human health such as insulin and growth hormones are produced in bacteria by recombinant DNA techniques. Recombinant DNA technology is used in developing gene therapies. The human genome project is a major endeavor to sequence the entire genome to identify new genes for both general understanding and specific medical applications. As more and more applications become available to humans, several ethical issues need to be considered and will be discussed later.

IV. SAFETY AND BIOETHICS

The major issues raised in recombinant DNA technology are related to the safety of both the scientists working in the laboratory and people consuming the product. Other issues include the ethical implications of both the development of such technology and its application on people.

A. Biological safety.

The safety guidelines for recombinant DNA techniques were developed by the NIH (National Institutes of Health) and are periodically updated. It is important to follow the safety rules in a molecular biology laboratory to avoid contamination, infection, and mistakes, which have the potential to replicate quickly before they are even realized. Other potential dangers in a molecular biology laboratory include chemicals that can interfere with DNA and cause mutations and pathogenic viruses. One should be aware of the different chemicals, bacteria, viruses, and other things used in a laboratory, and take adequate measures to protect laboratory workers from potential health hazards.

The safety to the public who are exposed to such recombinant products is regulated through the FDA, which studies each product rigorously for potential safety issues for the consumer. The industries also play a role in recommending certain procedures to be followed before approval. Some products or procedures involving the release of recombinant organisms into the environment are tested by the EPA (Environmental Protections Agency). However, some side effects may not be known until the product is available to the masses.

B. Ethical issues:

The ethical issues are critical in both the development and the implications of recombinant DNA technology as we saw before. It is important to consider before starting a project whether it is ethical to do such research. Examples include the use of fetal tissues for biological research and cloning humans by artificially replicating zygotes before implantation into surrogate mothers. Even though the techniques are available to do such research, especially the latter, it was stopped because of ethical concerns. The second issue is regarding the implications. For example, the availability of a vast amount of DNA sequence information on genetic diseases may prompt insurance agencies and employers to screen out people with potential genetic disorders. This is called genetic discrimination. How are we going to control the use and misuse of such information?

The examples of "Dolly" the sheep and "Gene" the cow that have been cloned from a single cell have raised serious concerns that it might lead to human cloning one day. Is it okay to have the technology and not use it, or should we just not start working on human cloning? Technologies are being developed to manufacture human body parts in laboratories to be used for transplantation. Is it ethical to use adult stem cells for research but not the embryonic stem cells? Time will tell how such ethical concerns will stay or change.

Made in the USA
Coppell, TX
08 September 2023